Developing Lit

POETRY COMPENDIUM

PHOTOCOPIABLE TEACHING RESOURCES
FOR LITERACY

ages
4–7

Christine Moorcroft

Series consultant Ray Barker

A & C BLACK

Contents

Acknowledgements

The author and publishers are grateful for permission to reproduce the following:

'The Bird' by Tony Mitton © 1996 Tony Mitton; 'Mudlarks' and 'Wet' from Out and About © 1988, 1998 Shirley Hughes and 'Green Lettuce, Green Peas' from Colours © 1986 Shirley Hughes, all reproduced by permission of the publisher Walker Books Ltd, London; 'This Finger's Straight' by Jack Ousbey, reproduced by permission of the author; 'The Forest Song' by Ian Sharp, reproduced by permission of the author; 'De Beat' by Grace Nichols, reproduced by permission of Curtis Brown Ltd, London, on behalf of Grace Nichols © 1998 Grace Nichols; 'The Horseman' by Walter de la Mare, reproduced by permission of the Literary Trustees of Walter de la Mare, and the Society of Authors as their representative; 'Jump or Jiggle' by Evelyn Beyer from Another Here and Now Story Book by Lucy Sprague Mitchell © 1937 by E. P. Dutton, renewed © 1965 by Lucy Sprague Mitchell, used by permission of Dutton Children's Books, an imprint of Penguin Books for Young Readers, a division of Penguin Putnam Inc.

Every effort has been made to trace copyright holders and to obtain their permission for use of copyright material. The author and publishers would be pleased to rectify in future editions any error or omission.

Published 2008 by A & C Black Publishers Limited
38 Soho Square, London W1D 3HB
www.acblack.com

ISBN: 978-1-4081-0052-3

Copyright text © Christine Moorcroft, 2001, 2008
Ages 4–5
Copyright illustrations © Gaynor Berry, 2001
Ages 5–6
Copyright illustrations © Michael Evans and Leon Baxter, 2001; pp 53, 58 Copyright illustrations © Gaynor Berry, 2001
Ages 6–7
Copyright illustrations © Kirsty Wilson, 2001
Copyright cover illustration © Sean Longcroft, 2008

The author and publishers would like to thank Ray Barker, Madeleine Madden, Kim Pérez and Julia Tappin for their advice in producing this series of books.

A CIP catalogue record for this book is available from the British Library.

Printed in Great Britain by Caligraving Ltd, Thetford, Norfolk.

This book is produced using paper that is made from wood grown in managed, sustainable forests. It is natural, renewable and recyclable. The logging and manufacturing processes conform to the environmental regulations of the country of origin.

Introduction

'If we know what we are doing when we teach poetry then we shall be secure: the rest of our work in English will follow by implication. Poetry is language used for its deepest and most fully exact purposes.'

David Holbrook, *English For Maturity*, Cambridge University Press, 1961

Many teachers are somewhat hesitant about introducing poetry into their classroom, perhaps remembering their own experiences in secondary school, where poetry was 'something to study' and the material related to the cultural tradition of poetry. Often poetry was seen as 'difficult' and old-fashioned. In the public domain it is often seen as something 'odd' and outside the current of normal life.

This reluctance should not be a problem in primary school. Young children enjoy poems; they enjoy reading them, talking about them and writing them. They enjoy the rhythms and sounds and patterns of poetry. Contemporary, experimental poets have helped in breaking down barriers around poetry, writing directly for young children in a language and style they can enjoy directly, but children's enjoyment is not limited to comic subjects and rhyme. Children need to be challenged by a range of subjects, forms and language. Poetry can offer a useful 'door to the past'. Of all art forms, it is 'most able to adapt itself to other epochs and other readerships.' (Laurence Lerner, *Reconstructing Literature*, Blackwell, 1983) A distinctive characteristic of poetry is its

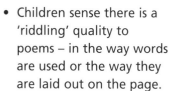

accessibility to all sorts of learners. Poems offer a range of choice, and are 'small' enough to be used in all classrooms for any amount of time.

Poems work differently from stories, creating effects and evoking responses which may overlap with the art of the story, but which are often peculiar to the nature of poetry.

- They are immediate; children will often 'get it' or not, more quickly. If some children don't 'get it', this means that poems will have to be read more than once.

- Children sense there is a 'riddling' quality to poems – in the way words are used or the way they are laid out on the page.

- Poems remind us about the creativity of language and young children are open enough to grasp that reader and poet meet on common ground – the ground of a shared language.

- Poems are 'multi-meaning' and there is not often a right answer to 'meaning'.

- Our responses to poetry are less linear than to a story. Poems are presented in a huge variety of ways and their job is not often to answer the question, 'What happens next?' Readers move around 'within' the poem for emotional impact or meaning.

- Poems provide 'experiences' and these are gained through a mixture of: the language used, the form, feelings communicated, detail used.

- Poetry was originally an oral form – stories and word-fun told and shared by others. It is not strictly a reading and writing activity. Poetry should be listened to as well – and often performed.

- Children can create poems more easily than a story and so achieve success. But poetry is not a one-off inspirational activity. It is something developmental and structured. You can create poems from ideas and then develop appropriate language and pattern around lists, from comparisons, from sounds, from stories.

Poetry activities in this series:

- are categorised to help you with planning – see the charts on pages 9, 50 and 91.

- are linked to the Primary Framework for Literacy.

- cover a wide range of forms and types of poetry – from a range of cultures and eras.

Using the activity sheets

Few resources are needed besides scissors, glue, word-banks and simple dictionaries. Access to ICT resources – computers, DVD, video, digital cameras, tape-recorders – would also be useful at times.

Brief teaching notes are provided at the bottom of each page – these can be masked before photocopying. More detailed notes and suggestions can be found in the **Notes on the activities** preceding each age group's activity sheets.

Most of the activity sheets end with a challenge (**Now try this!**) which reinforces and extends the children's learning and provides the teacher with an opportunity for assessment. These more challenging activities might be appropriate for only a few children; it is not expected that the whole class should complete them although many will be able to do so as a shared guided activity. On some pages there is space for the children to complete the extension activities, but for others they will need a notebook or a separate sheet of paper.

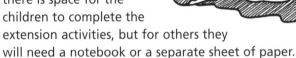

Ten things to think about when teaching poetry

Do you:

1   have a classroom containing a range of poetry resources, including anthologies, ICT, posters?

2   provide a range of challenging approaches and frameworks to writing that extend children's appreciation of poetry?

3   encourage children to look for writing opportunities in their own lives?

4   see writing as a process: gathering ideas, drafting, sharing and presentation?

5   vary approaches to writing in your class: pairs, groups, individuals, etc.?

6   have confidence that the class can be a critical audience for the work of others?

7   encourage children to read aloud and perform poems?

8   read aloud poetry to the class yourself on a regular basis?

9   see awareness of audience as essential to a piece of writing and find audiences for the work of the class, e.g. younger children, parents?

10   offer a range of possibilities for presenting material, e.g. ICT, creating anthologies, and for publication, e.g. the internet?

Assessment

The monitoring and assessment of poetry will depend upon the learning objectives set within any specific lesson; it is important to be clear about the nature of the aspect of poetry to be assessed. Teachers will also take into consideration some general principles, for example:

- Are you assessing the understanding of a principle, e.g. rhyme, simile – or are you assessing the quality of a written poem?

- In one sense, poetry is about the unassessable. The best poetry is unexpected, surprising and unpredictable.

- Any assessment needs to involve the reader and the audience, too.

- Is it more important that the child is developing increasing confidence in handling language or looking at the world in a more thoughtful, individual way?

Other activities in the series are ideal for the collection of evidence over the year and for the children to assess their own and each other's poetry. It is not expected that teachers will be able to assess all the class at any one time. It may be best to focus on a small group of children each week, although it may be possible to use the objectives for whole-class monitoring with certain activities. There should be opportunities for making comments and monitoring the children's ability in other subject areas over the week. However, all the information should be assimilated for an end-of-year summary which will enable easier transition and target-setting.

Notes on the activities

The notes below expand upon those provided at the bottom of the activity pages. They give ideas and suggestions for making the most of the activity sheet, including suggestions for the whole-class introduction, the plenary session or for follow-up work using an adapted version of the sheet. To help teachers to select appropriate learning experiences for their pupils, the activities are grouped into sections, but the pages need not be presented in the order in which they appear, unless stated otherwise.

Many of the activities suggest that the children memorise a poem, rhyme or verse. To help them in this, read it aloud and then repeat it, encouraging them to join in. Either display an enlarged copy of the poem, or work with a small group of children who each have their own copy to follow. Read a line, then cover it and ask the children to repeat the line, gradually building up the number of lines covered, until the children can recite the entire poem. The following mnemonic appears in several activities to remind the children how they can learn a poem:

Action poems

The activities in this section encourage the children to enact rhymes they hear or read. They also help them to appreciate the different rhythms of the poems and rhymes they hear.

Lullaby (page 11). This poem could be read as part of a collection of lullabies, with the children following the rhythm of the poem by moving a finger along the rocker of the cradle. They could make large paintings of lines to show the rhythm of a lullaby or they might paint pictures showing different types of rhythm: for example, a lively dance, a trotting horse, a speeding car or a bouncing ball. Compare the different paintings to guess the rhythms described.

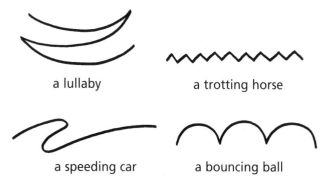

a lullaby

a trotting horse

a speeding car

a bouncing ball

See-saw, Margery Daw: 1 and **2** (pages 12–13). To introduce the 'see-saw' rhythm, show the children how to enact a see-saw by sitting in pairs on the floor with their feet touching, holding hands and rocking backwards and forwards. They could recite the rhyme as they go. They could also recite the rhyme (and their own versions of it) while moving model people up and down on ready-made see-saws or ones made from construction material.

Pat-a-cake, pat-a-cake (page 14). The children first clap their hands with the teacher as he or she reads the rhyme. Once they can clap their hands to the 'patting' rhythm, introduce other short poems and rhymes with a similar rhythm. The children could learn them and take turns to recite them, stopping and asking the rest of the class which word they have stopped on.

A hand mime (page 15). This page is designed to be read with a group or with the whole class. The pictures help the children to read and memorise the rhyme; they could do this with a partner. The children could make up their own hand mimes (which need not rhyme), for example:

Here is the lady's garden,

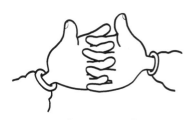

Here are the roots of the trees;

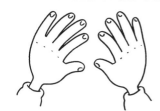

Here are the branches,

And here are the leaves.

The hand mimes could be performed in a 'shadow theatre': the children perform the hand actions behind a thin white cloth, such as a sheet, onto which a bright light is shone from behind them. The hands cast shadows onto the sheet which can be seen from the other side. **Do not let the children look directly into the light.**

Finger rhyme and **Finger puppets** (pages 16–17). After reading the rhyme and miming the actions, the children could choose a line to mime for a partner to identify and recite. In the extension activity, they could use different finger puppets and change the word 'fly' to 'run', 'creep', 'slide' and so on. They could also use these finger puppets as size-templates for making up their own. The simplest way to cut out the finger holes is to fold them into semi-circles before cutting:

The bird (page 18). The pictures help the children to read the poem, and the actions help them to memorise it. They could take turns to do the actions while other children recite the appropriate line.

The cat and **The elephant** (pages 19–20). These are based on **The bird** (page 18). The children make up poems in a similar format but about different animals.

Mix a pancake (page 21). This activity develops the children's appreciation of the rhythm of poems; they could compare its rhythm with that of other poems and rhymes, such as 'Pat-a-cake, pat-a-cake' (see page 14).

Ring-a-ring o'roses (page 22). Most children will know this nursery rhyme well, and should easily think up alternative endings even if they cannot write them. Examples they might come up with (or which the teacher could suggest) include: 'We all jump up', 'We all roll over', 'We all run fast' and 'We all stand still'. The children could take turns to tell the others what to do after 'A-tishoo'.

Question and answer poems

Many poems, chants and nursery rhymes have the format of 'question and answer'. In this section there are activities to help the children to recognise this structure, and to substitute questions and answers.

What are children made of? and **What are they made of? 1** and **2** (pages 23–25). The 'question and answer' arrangement of this rhyme makes it suitable for splitting into parts for groups or individuals to recite.

What's the time, Mr Wolf? (page 26). This simple poem has a repeating pattern with which the children soon become familiar. They could make up a variation by adding to the replies: for example, 'One o'clock – lunchtime' (the 'wolf' chases the 'sheep'), 'Four o'clock – time for football'.

Counting and alphabet poems

The poems, rhymes and chants in this section can be used to support work in mathematics as well as work on the recognition of words for numbers and the letters of the alphabet.

A mosquito one, a mosquito two and **Find the rhyme** (pages 27–28). These activities encourage the children to listen to the endings of words and to notice rhyme. The stamping, clapping or slapping helps them to appreciate the rhythm of the poem.

One potato, two potato (page 29). By trying out different words for foods to replace 'potato', the children also learn about rhythm and stress, even though these terms are not likely to be introduced (for example, 'cucumber' has the right number of syllables, but the stress is in the wrong place).

Alphabet rhymes (page 30). This activity develops the children's appreciation of rhythm and rhyme. They could build up rhyme-banks of words which rhyme with the appropriate letters. Some children might be able to change the rhyme so that it goes: a and b, Here is …, c and d, Here is …

Alphabet poem: 1 and **2** (pages 31–32). This activity develops the children's understanding of rhythm and rhyme and their knowledge of the alphabet. Point out that they should say the names of the letters rather than the sounds they make.

Repetition and choruses

In this section the children learn to recognise repeated language and to memorise it. Some of the activities develop their skills in recognising and predicting the changes in poems with patterned language.

Ee-aye-addio (page 33). Some children may recognise this popular football song. Other possible verses for the song could begin: 'We're going to win the league', 'United are the best' and 'We're going to win'.

Polly put the kettle on (page 34). This activity focuses on repetitive language. Draw the children's attention also to the sounds of the words (the repeated 'p' and 't' sounds in the first verse, and the repeated 'k' and 't' sounds in the second verse). Their own verses, using the examples provided, could end with, 'We'd all like a bite' and 'Wet soap suds'. Some children might be able to write their own rhymes.

Ee-aye-ee-aye-o: 1 and **2** (pages 35–36). This activity could be adapted to make up a new poem (for example, 'Old MacDonald had a zoo'), with appropriate animals. It asks for the conventional words for animal sounds (for example, 'cluck' and 'quack').

Word-play

The emphasis of this section is on the sounds and effects of words. It encourages the children to think of descriptive or expressive words and even to make up their own. It includes activities focusing on alliterative patterns and rhyme.

Messy mud (page 37). This prepares the children for later work on onomatopoeia: most of them will recognise the repeated 's' and 'p' sounds. Made-up words to describe mud with 'p' or 's' sounds could include: 'squerch', 'slup', 'plap'. The poem could be read aloud while playing with 'mud' made from flour mixed with water. Encourage the children to listen to the sounds made by hands (or feet, in rubber boots) slapping the mud. Their own poems could be lists of words or phrases to describe mud.

Crispy crunchy (page 38). If possible, provide pieces of celery for the children to snap while repeating the words 'crispy crunchy'. They could compare its texture with that of 'non-crispy crunchy' foods, such as yogurt and bread.

Thump, bump (page 39). Encourage the children to use the pictures as cues for the words they cannot read. Other things which go 'thump, bump' include heavy books falling, people tramping upstairs, something falling downstairs, the beat of loud pop music.

Hop to the shop (page 40). Several other activities have featured rhyme: here rhyme is the main focus of the activity. It links with phonics work on final sounds.

The children could also make up (orally) rhymes for things they do at school: for example, write by the light, read about a seed, eat the meat, bake a cake, look at a book. Possible answers for the extension activity are: go to a show, hug a big bug, fall on a ball, drink by the sink.

Sound pictures and **Sound cards** (pages 41–42). This activity requires the children to imagine the actual sounds made by the items, rather than the conventional words for the sounds. They should be able to read the sound cards using phonics, linking with work on reading and spelling strategies.

Animal sounds and **Outdoor sounds** (pages 43–44). Point to each picture in turn and ask the children to make the sound. Can the children find that sound on the page? The plenary session could consist of a game: give each group (of three or four) a card on which is stuck a picture of an animal cut from a magazine. Invite the children to take turns to make an animal sound. The group with the picture of that animal should reply with the same sound. It is then their turn to make another animal sound.

Morning and night poems: 1 and **2** (pages 45–46). Examples of poems the children could make up using the cards are:

Morning
Good morning
Wake up
Downstairs
Breakfast
Brush teeth
Off to school.

Night
Tea
Upstairs
Brush teeth
Bedtime story
Sleepy head
Good night.

Learning objectives

The following chart shows how the Ages 4–5 activity sheets (pages 11–46) match the Communication, language and literacy objectives of the Early Years Foundation Stage of the Primary Framework for Literacy (* means the objective is also an Early Learning Goal).

Objectives	Page numbers
Speaking	
Enjoy listening to and using spoken and written language and readily turn to it in play and learning	11–16, 18, 21, 23, 26, 27, 29, 30–40, 44–46
Use talk to organise, sequence and clarify thinking, ideas, feelings and events	45, 46
Use language to imagine and recreate roles and experiences	17, 19, 20, 22, 24–26, 36, 45, 46
Speak clearly and audibly with confidence and control and show awareness of the listener	17, 19, 20, 22, 24–26, 29, 30–34, 37, 45, 46
Extend their vocabulary, exploring the meanings and sounds of new words	19, 20, 22, 24, 25, 30, 36–44
Listening and responding	
* Listen with enjoyment and respond to stories, songs and other music, rhymes and poems and make up their own stories, songs, rhymes and poems	11–16, 18–27, 29, 31–37, 45, 46
* Sustain attentive listening, responding to what they have heard by relevant comments, questions or actions	11–16, 18–25, 27, 29, 33–37, 45, 46
* Extend their vocabulary, exploring meanings and sounds of new words	19, 20, 22, 24, 25, 27, 29–32, 36–44
Group discussion and interaction	
* Interact with others, negotiating plans and activities and taking turns in conversation	26, 31, 32, 35, 36, 39
Drama	
* Use language to imagine and recreate roles and experiences	17, 19, 20, 22, 24, 25, 35, 36

Objectives	Page numbers
Word recognition: decoding (reading) and encoding (spelling)	
* Explore and experiment with sounds, words and text	28–34, 37, 40, 45, 46
* Link sounds to letters, naming and sounding the letters of the alphabet	30, 31, 37
Read simple words by sounding out and blending the phonemes all through the word from left to right	40
Recognise common digraphs	40
* Read a range of familiar and common words and simple sentences independently	40
Word structure and spelling	
* Use phonic knowledge to write simple regular words and make phonetically plausible attempts at more complex words	31, 32
Understanding and interpreting texts	
* Know that print carries meaning and, in English, is read from left to right and top to bottom	11, 12, 14–16, 18, 22, 23, 27, 29, 33–37
* Extend their vocabulary, exploring the meaning and sounds of new words	19, 20, 22, 24, 25, 27, 29–32, 36–44
Engaging with and responding to texts	
* Listen with enjoyment to stories, songs, rhymes and poems, sustain attentive listening and respond with relevant comments, questions and actions	11–16, 18–25, 27, 29, 31–37
* Use language to imagine and recreate roles and experiences	17, 19, 20, 22, 24, 25
Creating and shaping texts/Text structure and organisation	
* Attempt writing for various purposes, using features of different forms such as lists, stories and instructions	19, 20, 22, 26, 31–34, 36

Lullaby

- **Say the lullaby.**

  With your finger, 'rock the cradle'.

Golden slumbers
Kiss your eyes,
Smiles await you
When you rise.
Sleep little baby,
Don't you cry,
And I shall sing a lullaby.

- **Draw some lines to show how the cradle rocks.**

Teachers' note Read the poem aloud with the children while they move a finger back and forth along the rocker of the cradle to the rocking rhythm of the poem. For the extension activity, the children draw lines which mimic the curve of the rocking of the cradle (see **Notes on the activities**, page 6). They should first practise 'drawing' the lines in the air with a finger.

Developing Literacy
Poetry Compendium:
Ages 4–7
© A & C BLACK

- **Say the rhyme.**

Move the see-saw up and down.

See-saw, Margery Daw,
Jacky shall have a new master;
He shall have but a penny a day,
Because he can't work any faster.

- **Change the rhyme.**

Say your name instead.

- **Say your new rhyme.**

Teachers' note The children need the see-saw on page 13. Read (or chant) the poem aloud with the children. Help them to move the see-saw up and down to the rhythm of the poem. If you have a see-saw in school they could first take turns on it while the others say the poem. In the extension activity the children should insert their own name instead of 'Jacky' and see if it fits the rhythm.

Developing Literacy Poetry Compendium: Ages 4–7
© A & C BLACK

See-saw, Margery Daw: 2

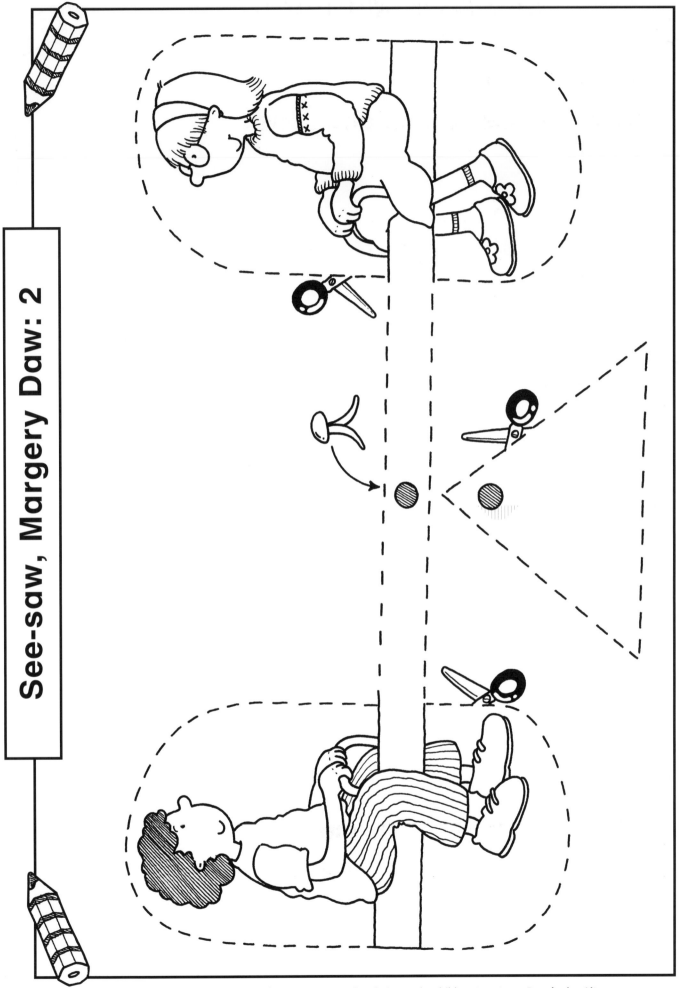

Teachers' note Use this with page 12. Copy the page onto card and give to the children to cut around the dotted lines. Fix the see-saw to the base using a split pin as a pivot.

Developing Literacy
Poetry Compendium:
Ages 4–7
© A & C BLACK

13

Pat-a-cake, pat-a-cake

- **Say the rhyme.**

  Clap the rhythm.

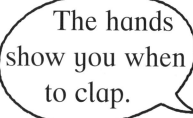 The hands show you when to clap.

Pat - a - cake, pat - a - cake, baker's man,

Bake me a cake as fast as you can;

Pat it and prick it, and mark it with B;

Put it in the oven for Baby and me.

 Now try this!

- **Learn the rhyme.**

 Look and read    Cover   Say   Check

---

Teachers' note Although the children will not have learned about syllables, most of them will be able to clap their hands to each beat of this simple rhythm (the hands depicted beneath the words will help). Read the rhyme aloud, clapping your hands (the children clapping, too) and stop part-way through a line. Ask the children which word you have stopped on.

Developing Literacy
Poetry Compendium:
Ages 4–7
© A & C BLACK

A hand mime

- **Say the rhyme.**

  Do the actions.

The pictures show you what to do.

 Here are the lady's knives and forks,

 Here is the lady's table,

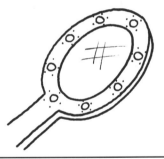 Here is the lady's looking-glass,

 And here is the baby's cradle.

 • **Learn the rhyme.**

 Look and read   **Cover**   **Say**   **Check**

Teachers' note Read the rhyme aloud with the children; demonstrate the hand mime and encourage the children to try it. They could mime one line of the rhyme for a friend to identify and recite.

Developing Literacy
Poetry Compendium:
Ages 4–7
© A & C BLACK

Finger rhyme

- **Say the rhyme.**

  Use the finger puppets.

Two little dicky birds
Sitting on a wall,

One named Peter

And one named Paul.

Fly away, Peter!

Fly away, Paul!

Come back, Peter!

Come back, Paul!

- **Change the rhyme.**

  Use different finger puppets.

Teachers' note Use this page with the finger puppets on page 17. Many children will already know this familiar rhyme; encourage them to recite it and do the actions: they begin with a 'dicky bird' finger puppet on each hand, hold up each one as it is introduced (making it look as if it is sitting on a wall), then they make the birds fly away and come back.

**Developing Literacy
Poetry Compendium:
Ages 4–7
© A & C BLACK**

16

Finger puppets

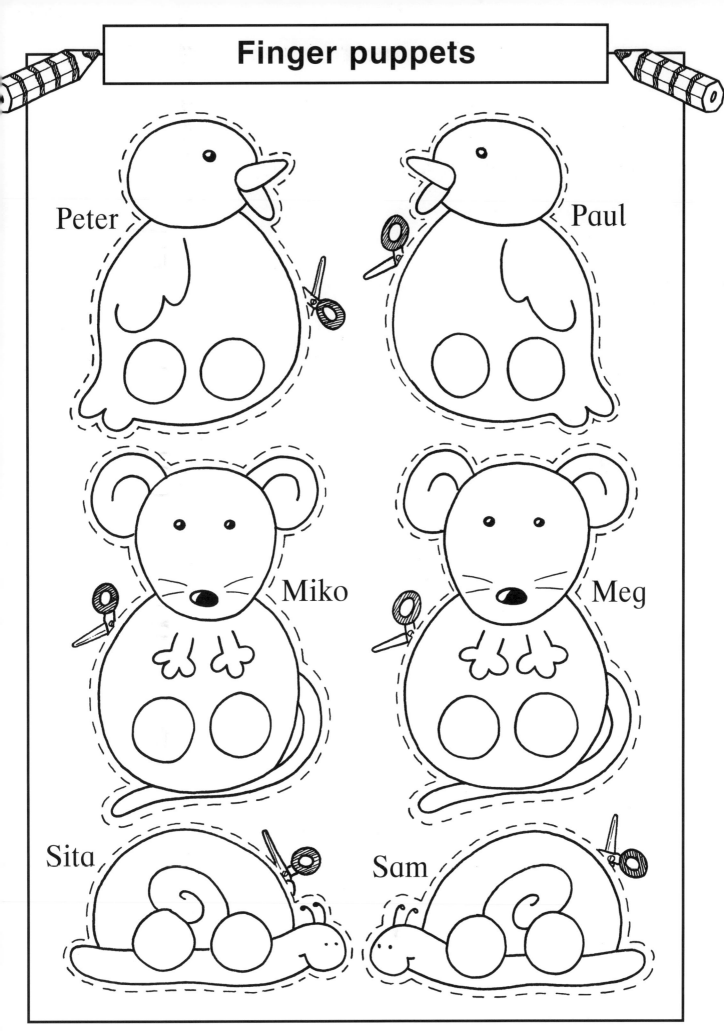

Peter

Paul

Miko

Meg

Sita

Sam

Teachers' note Use these finger puppets with page 16. Copy the page onto card and give to the children to cut out the outlines. They will need help in cutting the finger holes (see **Notes on the activities**, page 7, for a simple way to cut them out). The children say their finger rhymes to a friend. Encourage them to try out their ideas aloud with the puppets.

Developing Literacy Poetry Compendium: Ages 4–7 © A & C BLACK

The bird

• **Say the poem.**

  Do the actions.

Actions

Here are the legs that walk along.	 
Here is the beak that sings a song.	 
Here are the wings that flap and spread.	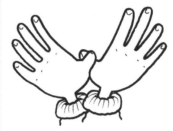 
And here is the bird above my head. Tony Mitton	 

Now try this!

• **Cut out the words and pictures.**
• **Mix them up for a friend to match.**

Teachers' note The sections of the poem should not be cut out until the extension activity is reached. Read the poem aloud to the children; read it again and encourage them to join in and do the actions. Help them to memorise it (see **Notes on the activities**, page 6).

Developing Literacy
Poetry Compendium:
Ages 4–7
© A & C BLACK

The cat

Make up a poem about a cat.

• **Choose words to fill the gaps.**

• **Do the actions.**

It doesn't have to rhyme.

paws

pad   pat

tap

Here are the _____

that _____

_____

tail

flips   flaps

flicks

Here is the _____

that _____

_____

whiskers

tickle   wiggle

waggle

Here are the _____

that _____

_____

Now try this!

• **Make up verses about the cat's**

 ears **and** eyes **.**

Do the actions.

Teachers' note Discuss the movements of a cat to help the children to choose the best word for the way in which it uses each part of its body. They should read their poems aloud, doing the actions. Examples of the responses which the children might make are: Here are the paws that pad along; Here is the tail that flicks the air; Here are the whiskers that tickle my face.

**Developing Literacy
Poetry Compendium:
Ages 4–7
© A & C BLACK**

The elephant

Make up a poem about an elephant.

- **Fill in the gaps.**

- **Do the actions.**

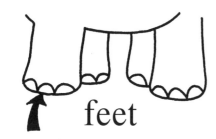

feet

Here are the _____ that

_____

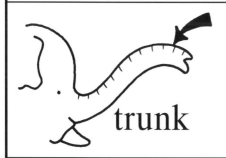

trunk

Here is the _____ that

_____

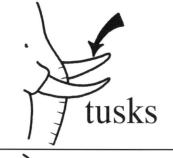

tusks

Here are the _____ that

_____

tail

Here is the _____ that

_____

Now try this!

- **Make up a poem about**

  another animal.

Teachers' note Discuss the movements of an elephant to help the children to choose the best word for the way in which it uses each part of its body. They should read their poems aloud, doing the actions. Examples of the responses which the children might make are: Here are the feet that stamp along; Here is the trunk that waves about.

Developing Literacy
Poetry Compendium:
Ages 4–7
© A & C BLACK

• **Say the rhyme.**

Do the actions.

Mix a pancake,

stir a pancake,

pop it in a pan.

Fry the pancake,

toss the pancake,

catch it if you can!

• **Learn the rhyme.**

 Look and read **Cover** **Say** **Check**

Work with a friend.

Teachers' note Read the poem while enacting 'stirring' or 'mixing' pancake mixture; repeat the first two lines, while the children join in and mime the stirring of the pancake mixture, to help them to appreciate its rhythm. Change the tone and rhythm of your voice to indicate the adventurous tossing of the pancake (look upwards for 'toss the pancake' and 'catch it if you can!').

**Developing Literacy
Poetry Compendium:
Ages 4–7
© A & C BLACK**

Ring-a-ring o'roses

- **Say the rhyme.**

  Do the actions.

Ring-a-ring o'roses,
A pocket full of posies,
A-tishoo! A-tishoo!
We all fall down.

- **Make up two new endings.**
- **Draw the pictures.**

Ring-a-ring o'roses, A pocket full of posies, A-tishoo! A-tishoo! We all _____ _____.	
Ring-a-ring o'roses, A pocket full of posies, A-tishoo! A-tishoo! _____	

Now try this!

- **Say the new rhymes.**

  Do the actions.

Teachers' note The children could enact the rhyme if a large enough area is available; skipping in a ring to the first two lines and dropping to the ground for the next two. Encourage them to make up their own new endings orally, and enact them, before they begin the activity sheet.

**Developing Literacy
Poetry Compendium:
Ages 4–7**
© A & C BLACK

What are children made of?

- **Say the rhyme.**

What are naughty children made of, made of?

What are naughty children made of?

Slugs and snails

And puppy-dogs' tails,

That's what naughty children are made of.

What are good children made of, made of?

What are good children made of?

Sugar and spice

And all things nice,

That's what good children are made of.

- **Learn the rhyme.**

Look and read   **Cover**   **Say**   **Check**

- **What else could children be made of?**
- **Make up your own rhyme.**

Teachers' note Read the rhyme. Repeat it with the children joining in. They could read the rhyme with a friend; one asking the questions and the other giving the answers (using the words supplied on pages 24 and 25 and thinking up others of their own).

Developing Literacy Poetry Compendium: Ages 4–7 © A & C BLACK

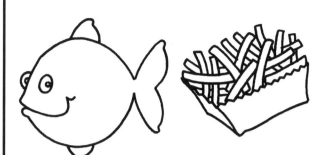

Fish and chips

and apple pips

Plums and pears

and teddy bears

Pins and cogs

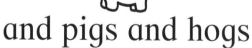

and pigs and hogs

The moon and stars

and candy bars

Teachers' note Cut the page into separate cards as indicated. Use the cards with pages 23 and 25. The cards could be mixed up and the children could find the matching rhyme for each one.

Developing Literacy
Poetry Compendium:
Ages 4–7
© A & C BLACK

Cats and dogs

and worms and frogs

Bugs and flies

and apple pies

Mops and rags

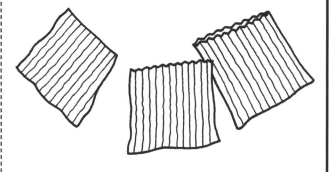

and paper bags

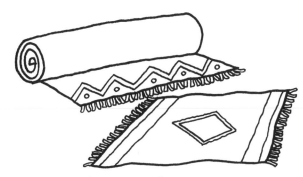

Big red rugs

and kisses and hugs

Teachers' note Cut the page into separate cards as indicated. Use the cards with pages 23 and 24.

Developing Literacy Poetry Compendium: Ages 4–7
© A & C BLACK

What's the time, Mr Wolf?

- **Fill in the gaps.**
- **Say the poem with your group.**

  Take turns to be the sheep and the wolf.

What's the time, Mr Wolf?

One o'clock.

What's the time, _____?

Four _____.

- **Make up a new poem.**
- **Take turns to be the wolf.**

Now try this!

Teachers' note For the extension activity provide some of the children (the wolves) in a group with clock faces with moveable hands. The other children take turns to ask one of the wolves the time, to develop the poem. They then swap roles and repeat. They could vary the poem by answering 'Bedtime' or 'Dinnertime'.

**Developing Literacy
Poetry Compendium:
Ages 4–7
© A & C BLACK**

A mosquito one, a mosquito two

- **Say the rhyme. Do the actions.**

A mosquito one, a mosquito two,

A mosquito jump in the old man shoe.

A mosquito three, a mosquito four,

A mosquito open the old man door.

A mosquito five, a mosquito six,

A mosquito pick up the old man sticks.

A mosquito seven, a mosquito eight,

A mosquito open the old man gate.

A mosquito nine, a mosquito ten,

A mosquito biting the man again.

- **Learn the rhyme.**

Look and read   Cover   Say   Check

- **Say the rhyme with a friend.**

Teachers' note Read the rhyme, showing the children how to make the numbers with their fingers and thumbs (as shown in the illustrations). Read it again, demonstrating when to slap the floor, clap hands or stamp feet on the beat (indicated by the stars). Read it once more: see if they can combine both actions – showing the numbers and slapping, clapping or stamping on the beat.

**Developing Literacy
Poetry Compendium:
Ages 4–7
© A & C BLACK**

Find the rhyme

• **Match the numbers to the words.**

2 two

4 four

6 six

8 eight

10 ten

ticks

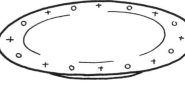

plate

hen

zoo

saw

Now try this!

• **With a friend, make up another mosquito rhyme.**
• **Say it together.**

Teachers' note The children should first complete the activity on page 27. After finding the rhyming words for the numbers, the children make up their own versions of the rhyme 'A mosquito one, a mosquito two'. Encourage them to show the numbers with their fingers and thumbs and slap, clap or stamp on the beat.

Developing Literacy Poetry Compendium: Ages 4–7 © A & C BLACK

One potato, two potato

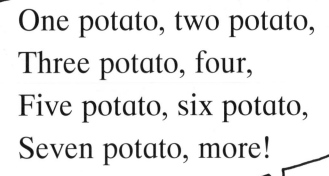

> One potato, two potato,
> Three potato, four,
> Five potato, six potato,
> Seven potato, more!

- **Say the rhyme.**
- **Say another food, instead of 'potato'.**
- **Does it have the same rhythm? ✓ or ✗**

samosa	banana	cherry	spaghetti
☐	☐	☐	☐

tomato	pea	chapatti	pear
☐	☐	☐	☐

Now try this!

- **Say the rhyme with other foods.**
- **Draw and write the foods which have the same rhythm.**

Teachers' note After reading the rhyme, encourage the children to try out the names of the different foods in place of the word 'potato' and to say which ones sound right. Point out the rhythm. Other foods for their own rhymes include: fish finger, chip butty, cream cracker and cheese sandwich.

Developing Literacy
Poetry Compendium:
Ages 4–7
© A & C BLACK

Alphabet rhymes

- **Say the names of these letters.**
- **Join each letter in a circle to a word that rhymes.**

a, b, (c)   d, e, (f)   g, h, (i)

Here is a bell.	Here is a key.	Here is a car.

Here is Jeff.	Here is a pie.	Here is a toe.

j, k, (l)   m, n, (o)   p, q, (r)

- **Make up rhymes for these.**

s and (t)	u and (v)	w and (x)	y and (z)

Teachers' note Most children should be able to work on this activity independently. The pictures and the repetition of 'Here is a …' help them to read it unaided, and provide a pattern which they can follow for their own alphabet rhyme. During the plenary session a group could recite the whole alphabet in rhyme.

Developing Literacy
Poetry Compendium:
Ages 4–7
© A & C BLACK

Alphabet poem: 1

a b c d e f g h i j k l m
n o p q r s t u v w x y z

- **With a friend, say and clap.**

- **Fill in the gaps.**

You say	Your friend says

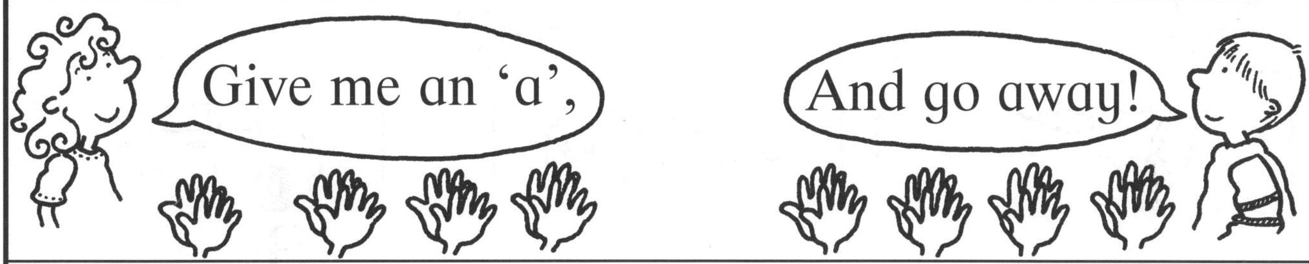

Give me an 'a',

And go away!

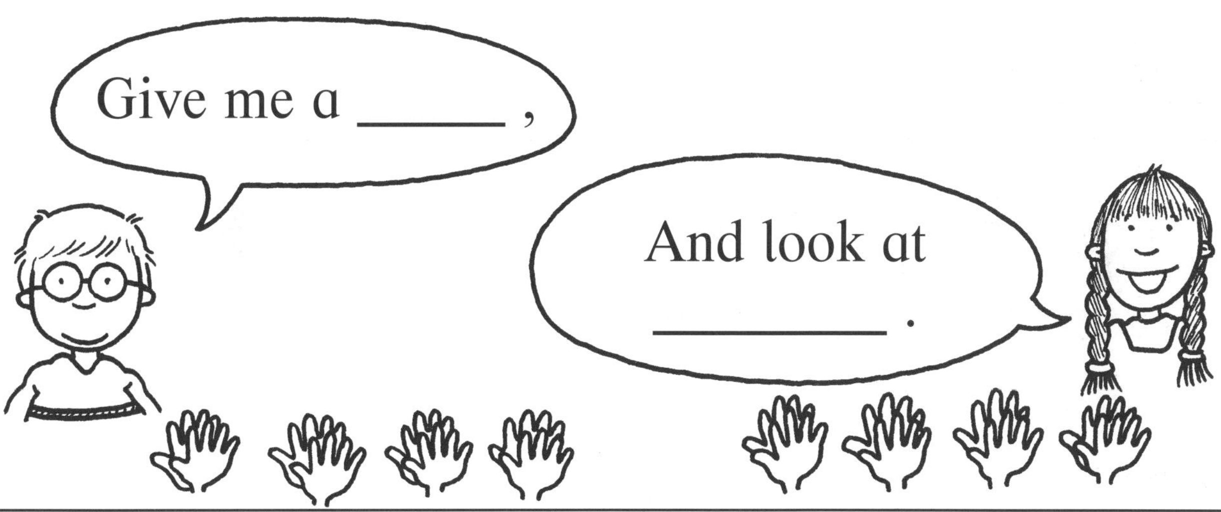

Give me a _____ ,

And look at _____ .

Give me a _____ ,

And have some _____ .

Teachers' note Show the children how to clap on each syllable as they recite the invitation (You) and response (Your friend says). Ask them to swap parts so that they each have a chance to make up the rhymes. Continued on page 32.

Developing Literacy
Poetry Compendium:
Ages 4–7
© A & C BLACK

Alphabet poem: 2

- **With your friend, say your alphabet poem.**

Teachers' note Use this with page 31. The children could continue through the alphabet (without necessarily writing each invitation and response). Different groups could work on different sets of letters so that, during the plenary session, the whole alphabet is recited with rhyming words for each letter.

Developing Literacy
Poetry Compendium:
Ages 4–7
© A & C BLACK

Ee-aye-addio

- **Say the football song.**

> We won the cup!
> We won the cup!
> Ee-aye-addio,
> We won the cup!

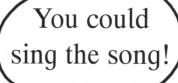

You could sing the song!

- **Fill in the gaps.**

We want a goal!
We want a goal!

_____

_____

What a great shot!
What a great shot!

_____

_____

- **Say the song.**

- **Make up another verse for the song.**

Teachers' note Different groups could recite or sing the verses of the football song, including any they have made up, with the whole class joining in the chorus.

Developing Literacy
Poetry Compendium:
Ages 4–7
© A & C BLACK

Polly put the kettle on

- **Say the poem.**
- **Fill in the gaps.**

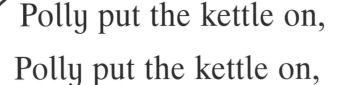

Polly put the kettle on,

Polly put the kettle on,

Polly put _____ ,

We'll all have tea.

Sukey take it off again,

Sukey _____ ,

_____ ,

They've all gone away.

- **Make up other verses.**

Becky bake some biscuits,

William wash the dishes,

Teachers' note Read the poem to the children and then repeat it, stopping for them to supply the repeated words. In the extension activity encourage them to read and repeat the first lines provided. They should re-read the last line of each of the previous verses before making up their own.

**Developing Literacy
Poetry Compendium:
Ages 4–7
© A & C BLACK**

- **Say the chorus.**

Ee-aye-ee-aye-o!

- **Say the verse.**

- **Write each chorus.**

Old MacDonald had a farm,

And on that farm he had a cow,

With a moo-moo here and a moo-moo there,
Here a moo, there a moo,
Everywhere a moo-moo,
Old MacDonald had a farm,

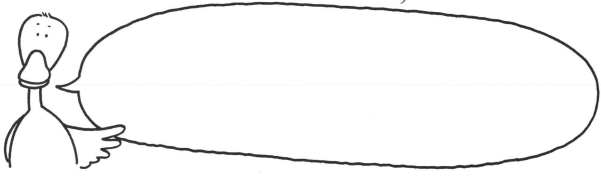

Teachers' note The poem can be read by the whole class, in groups, with an adult reading the first line, the whole class joining in the chorus, individuals introducing each animal and their own group making the sound of the animal. Continued on page 36.

**Developing Literacy
Poetry Compendium:
Ages 4–7**
© A & C BLACK

Old MacDonald had a farm,

And on that farm he had a hen,

With a cluck-cluck here and a

_____ ,

Here a _____ , there a _____ ,

Everywhere a _____ ,

Old MacDonald had a farm,

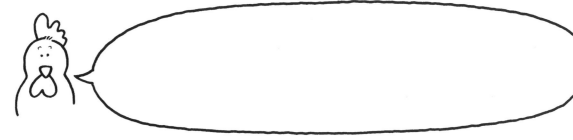

- **Make up verses for these.**

 a sheep   a duck  a horse

- **Say your verses to a friend.**

Teachers' note Use this with page 35. Individuals could read the verses they have made up, with the whole class joining in the chorus.

Developing Literacy Poetry Compendium: Ages 4–7 © A & C BLACK

Messy mud

- **Say the poem. Listen for** $\boxed{\text{s}}$.
- **Circle the words with** $\boxed{\text{s}}$.

I like mud.
The slippy, sloppy,
   squelchy kind,
The slap-it-into-pies kind.
Stir it up in puddles,
Slither and slide.
I *do* like mud.

Shirley Hughes

- **Say the poem again.**

  Listen for $\boxed{\text{p}}$.

- **Write the words with** $\boxed{\text{p}}$.

_____   _____   _____

_____   _____   _____

Now try this!

- **Make up your own 'mud' words.**

  Use $\boxed{\text{s}}$ **and** $\boxed{\text{p}}$.

- **Say your words to a friend.**

Teachers' note Read the poem to the children (it is not intended that they should try to read it for themselves, although many of them will manage the first and last lines). Re-read it, pausing for the children to repeat each line. Ask them what they notice about the sounds (the words sound like mud squelching).
'Mudlarks' from *Out and About* © 1988, 1998 Shirley Hughes

Developing Literacy
Poetry Compendium:
Ages 4–7
© A & C BLACK

Crispy crunchy

• **Say the words.**

> crispy crunchy, crispy crunchy,
> crispy crunchy, crispy crunchy

• **Which things are crispy crunchy?** ✓ **or** ✗

banana ☐	jelly ☐	apple ☐
crisps ☐	cornflakes ☐	milk ☐

• **Draw and label two other crispy crunchy things.**

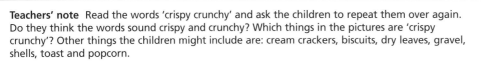

Now try this!

Teachers' note Read the words 'crispy crunchy' and ask the children to repeat them over again. Do they think the words sound crispy and crunchy? Which things in the pictures are 'crispy crunchy'? Other things the children might include are: cream crackers, biscuits, dry leaves, gravel, shells, toast and popcorn.

Developing Literacy
Poetry Compendium:
Ages 4–7
© A & C BLACK

Thump, bump

- **Take turns to roll the dice.**

- **Move your counter.**

- **Look and read.**

- **Does it go 'thump, bump'?**

  | yes | roll the dice again |

  | no | stop |

You need

a dice

four counters

Start

a big boot

a snowflake

a cat

an elephant

rain

a big hammer

a bird

a mouse

rocks

a football

leaves

a fight

a feather

a fly

a lorry

Finish

Now try this!

- **Draw and label two other things which go 'thump, bump'.**

Teachers' note This game for four players develops appreciation of the qualities of sounds. Introduce the activity with 'thump, bump' sounds by hitting a table top with the side of a fist. Look at the board game with the children and name the objects in turn. If its sound is 'thump, bump' the children shout 'THUMP, BUMP!'; if not, they whisper 'Not thump, bump'.

**Developing Literacy
Poetry Compendium:
Ages 4–7
© A & C BLACK**

Hop to the shop

- **Write words that rhyme.**

Time for a rhyme!

hop to the *shop*

Word-bank

hay

king

ship

sky

sun

skip to the _____

run in the _____

fly in the _____

sing to the _____

play in the _____

- **Make up rhymes for these.**

Now try this!

| go | hug | fall | drink |

Teachers' note Ask the children what they notice about the sounds of 'time for a rhyme' and 'hop to the shop'. After they have completed the activity sheet, encourage them to read and repeat each rhyming sound they have written. They could think of alternative rhyming words: for example, hop with a mop and run with a bun.

Developing Literacy
Poetry Compendium:
Ages 4–7
© A & C BLACK

Sound pictures

drums

trotting horse

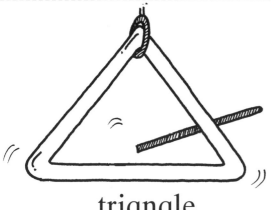

triangle

paintbrush

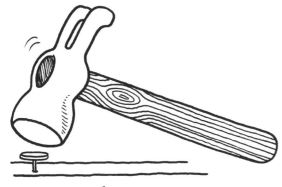

hammer

police car

boots in puddles

dripping tap

Teachers' note Use this with page 42. The children cut out the sound pictures and, working with a partner or in a small group, match them to the sound cards. They could also play 'matching pairs' with both sets of cards: spread them out face down and ask the children to take turns to turn over two cards. If the sound matches the picture, they keep the pair.

**Developing Literacy
Poetry Compendium:
Ages 4–7**
© A & C BLACK

41

Sound cards

da da dum, da da dum	clip, clop, clip, clop
ting, tang, ting, tang	slop, slap, slop, slap
tap, tap tap, tap	nee-na, nee-na
splish, splosh splish, splosh	drip, drop drip, drop

Teachers' note Use this with page 41. The children cut out the sound cards and match them to the sound pictures. Help them to read the words for sounds by sounding out the graphemes.

Developing Literacy Poetry Compendium: Ages 4–7 © A & C BLACK

Animal sounds

• **Join the animals to the sounds.**

Developing Literacy
Poetry Compendium:
Ages 4–7
© A & C BLACK

• **Make sounds for other animals.**

• **Ask a friend to guess what they are.**

Teachers' note If possible, combine this activity with observations of real animals, or recordings of them. The children can listen to the sound of each animal and make the sound themselves. They could also make up silly rhymes about the animals: for example, 'Woof,' said the dog as he chopped a log; 'Meow,' said the cat as she put on her hat.

Outdoor sounds

• **Join the pictures to the sounds.**

swish, swish

waaaah

brum, brum

beep, beep

crash, smash

• **Say the sounds for other things.**

• **Ask a friend to guess what they are.**

Teachers' note If possible, combine this activity with a walk around the local area, or let the children listen to recordings of sounds heard outdoors. The children can listen to each sound and then try to make the sound themselves.

Developing Literacy
Poetry Compendium:
Ages 4–7
© A & C BLACK

- **Cut out the cards.**

- **Make up a morning poem.**

- **Make up a night poem.**

- **Say your poems.**

Sleep

Breakfast

Upstairs

Brush teeth

Sleepy head

Time to go out

Tea

Time to come in

Teachers' note Use this with page 46. Ask the children (working with a partner or in a small group) to sort the cards into 'morning' and 'night'. Some of the cards could be placed in either set: encourage the children to discuss their sorting and to say why the cards belong in a particular set.

**Developing Literacy
Poetry Compendium:
Ages 4–7**
© A & C BLACK

Good morning

Good night

Wash face

Downstairs

Bedtime story

Bedtime clothes

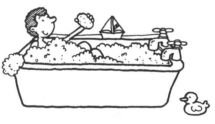

Bath-time

Wake up

Toast

Off to school

Teachers' note Use this with page 45. When the children have sorted the cards, ensure that they can read the words on them. They choose some of them to arrange as a poem (you could limit them to four or five cards). Ask them to read their poems aloud and to decide if they want to change them.

Developing Literacy Poetry Compendium: Ages 4–7 © A & C BLACK

Notes on the activities

The notes below expand upon those provided at the bottom of the activity pages. They give ideas and suggestions for making the most of the activity sheet, including suggestions for the whole-class introduction, the plenary session or for follow-up work using an adapted version of the sheet. The activities are grouped into units in line with the Primary Framework for Literacy, but the pages need not be presented in the order in which they appear, unless stated otherwise.

Many of the activities suggest that the children memorise a poem, rhyme or verse. To help them in this, read it aloud and then repeat it, encouraging them to join in. Either display an enlarged copy of the poem, or work with a small group of children who each have their own copy to follow. Read a line, then cover it and ask the children to repeat the line, gradually building up the number of lines covered, until the children can recite the entire poem. The following mnemonic appears in several activities to remind the children how they can learn a poem:

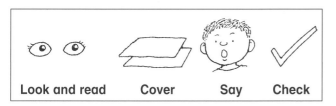

| Look and read | Cover | Say | Check |

Unit 1: Using the senses

The activities in this section introduce poems, rhymes and chants in which the children use their senses: for example, to listen for particular sounds or to enact the meaning and rhythm. A few of the poems they are asked to read or write are about the senses. To help the children to appreciate rhythm, give them opportunities to clap, tap or stamp their feet to the rhythm as appropriate and even to jump in the air on stressed words.

This finger's straight (page 52). The children could learn the rhyme, a line at a time, as the teacher mimes it with his or her fingers. Provide books in which they could look for other finger rhymes: for example, *Tickle My Nose* (Kaye Umansky and Nick Sharratt, Puffin) and *Finger Rhymes* (John Foster and Carol Thompson, OUP).

Ride-a-cock-horse (page 53). This poem could be read as part of a collection of 'trotting' poems, with the children following the rhythm of the poem by 'trotting' their fingers along pairs of hoof-prints.

If the materials are prepared beforehand, they could make potato or sponge prints of the hoof-prints while they recite the 'trotting' poems or create the rhythm using percussion instruments.

Point and read (page 54). The children learn to associate the spoken with the written word as they read this familiar rhyme and point to the words. Display other rhymes they know (at a height they can reach) and encourage them to point to the words as they read them.

Hair and **Eyes** (pages 55–56). The poem 'Hair' is interesting for its changes in rhythm: the quick rhythm of the first four lines, and the emphatic fifth line followed by a pause, repeated in the next four lines. The rhyming pattern emphasises this rhythm (the lines which are followed by a pause rhyme). For the activity on page 56, the children should model their own poem about eyes on the rhythm of 'Hair'.

Wet poem (page 57). After reading the poem to the children, ask them how the poet has made it sound 'wet': which words have a 'wet' sound? They could make a list of 'wet words' (for example, sloppy, slushy, water, run, rush) and notice which sounds can be heard in many of them.

Crazy creatures (page 58). This links with phonics work on initial consonant sounds. The children could also make up nicknames for animals: Freddy Fish, Gerry Giraffe, Fergus Fox, Rosie Rat. They could think of animals which begin with the same letter as their own name or those of friends.

Unit 2: Pattern and rhyme

This section features poetry in which there is a chorus, in which words or lines are repeated, or which has a pattern (such as lines beginning in a similar way: for example 'There I saw…' and 'I went…'). The children can learn about rhyme by playing with words – changing the initial sound to discover the words they can produce which rhyme.

Picture jingle (page 59). The children could draw (and paint) pictures to illustrate other silly rhymes (for example, 'Hey Diddle, Diddle, the Cat and the Fiddle', 'Jack be Nimble' and 'Sally Go Round the Sun'). Two other jingles, which are less familiar, are:

> Hoddley, poddley, puddle and frogs,
> Cats are to marry the poodle dogs:
> Cats in blue jackets and dogs in red hats,
> What will become of the mice and the rats?
>
> and

Hokey, pokey, diddley dat,
How do you like your potatoes done?
Boiled in water, fried in fat,
How do you like your potatoes done?

Jingle kit: 1 and **2** (pages 60–61). The children should model their 'silly jingles' on the one on page 59. They could make up others of their own (although it will be difficult to find  two-syllable words with which to end the third and fourth lines – let them use one-syllable words such as chair/air, floor/door, path/bath, sink/drink).

There I saw (page 62). The children might need help in imitating the pattern of this poem. Ask them to name a place (for example, a beach) and then to think of a word to describe it (for example, 'sandy'): 'I went down to the sandy beach'. Ask them what they saw (for example, a crab) and help them to think of a word for what it was like (for example, 'scrabbling' or 'scuttling'). The activity could be carried out after the class has been taken for a walk, during which the children could chant parts of the poem as they see things. This could be linked with sentence structure work on prepositions and descriptive words.

Eat brown bread (page 63). The children could change the rhyme, using the names of other kinds of sausages they know, such as banger, chipolata, liverwurst, or other kinds of vegetable or fruit.

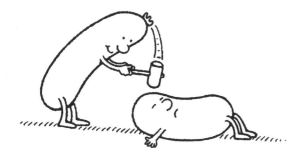

Eat fish and chips (page 64). This activity develops the rhyme-building activity on page 63. As a further extension activity, encourage the children to experiment with other rhymes.

The forest song: 1 and **2** (pages 65–66). During a music lesson the children could make up tunes for this song, using percussion instruments. Point out the change in rhythm: the song begins with a marching rhythm, which changes to a skipping

rhythm for the chorus. The verses they make up could be collected and pasted into a class book, to which they could add verses at later dates.

Far star (page 67). This activity can be linked with phonics work on rhyming words. The children could also listen for rhymes in other poems and in songs they hear on television and the radio.

Rub-a-dub-dub (page 68). This activity develops the children's understanding of rhyme, rhythm and pattern by asking them to make substitutions in this familiar nursery rhyme while keeping to the rhythm and pattern of the poem. They could also make up rhymes in which the three men are in a lorry, a plane, a tractor or a rocket. The verses could be written on outlines of the vehicles and displayed.

The rhyme shop (page 69). This activity introduces the list form for poems. The children might be able to make up rhymes for things they and their friends and families might buy (this could be extended to other commodities as well as food). Encourage them to say their rhymes to a partner. They will then be able to think up many more than if they are restricted to writing them.

Pirates' shopping list (page 70). This develops the children's appreciation of the list form for poems by providing a format with an appropriate shape. The pictures and captions offer some prompts for ideas for their poems.

A week at the shops (page 71). This activity introduces the children to the diary form for poems. The children should notice the pattern of the poem: the words which stay the same in each verse and those which change. They should be able to work out which day of the week should be in each verse and match the goods to the shops using the pictures as prompts.

Question and answer poem (page 72). Here the children meet a third simple poetic form: the question and answer poem. This poem could be sung to the tune of 'Ding, Dong, Bell'. The activity can be linked to sentence structure work on question marks. Encourage the children to think up humorous or even magical responses to the questions.

Unit 3: Poems on a theme

As well as appreciating the sounds of the words, rhythm, rhyme and other poetic devices, the children need to experience poems which say something about a topic. This section focuses on the meanings of poems and the topics about which poets write.

One happy bear and **Poem spinners: 1** and **2** (pages 73–75). These pages offer the children an opportunity to read a number poem and then create counting poems of their own. They should notice the repeated pattern of the poem, the rhyming words and the 'half-rhyme' or assonance of 'leaf' and 'underneath'. Their own poems, constructed using the spinners, will have the same rhythm but will not rhyme. More imaginative results could be encouraged by carrying out the activity orally: provide interesting objects (or pictures of them) about which the children can make up verses: for example, flowers, jewellery, fabrics, unusual or beautiful clothes, ornaments and pictures of animals, landscapes, towers, standing stones, waterfalls and volcanoes.

Ten fat sausages (page 76). Point out that this number poem is also about food, a common theme of children's poetry. The children should notice the repeated pattern and language of the poem. After this activity they could make a personal anthology of counting songs (for counting forwards and backwards).

Countdown wheels (page 77). This activity develops the children's skills in imitating the rhythm and pattern of a poem. Once they have selected an object and what it was doing, they need to make up what happened to two of them in each verse to be eliminated from the song.

Zany zoo (page 78). The children are encouraged here to play with words, making up alliterative animal names. This can be linked with text-level revision on writing captions. During an art lesson the children could paint pictures of animals based on observations of books,  television programmes, videos and real life; they could write nicknames as captions for their pictures. They could also make up 'same-letter' nicknames for people (no unkind ones).

Weather words (page 79). This prepares the children for later activities on weather poems while developing their awareness of the initial sounds of words. They could also compile their own collections of 'same start words' for use in their writing.

List poem notebook (page 80). Encourage the children to use their own word-banks as well as this notebook when they are writing. At this stage many words will need to be supplied to get them started; provide information books, fiction and poetry books about the weather and introduce interesting words to describe the weather during any daily observations which are made by the children. Make a note of words used in weather forecasts and display them; the children could add to the collection.

List poem (page 81). The children can use this page as a template to draw and write their own list poem. They need to collect ideas for their poems first, in the form of notes (see **List poem notebook** on page 80). You could re-read the poem 'Wet' on page 57 with the children and point out that this is an example of a list poem about the weather.

When I was... 1, **2** and **3** (pages 82–84). The children could contribute to a word-bank of things they were able to do at different ages before creating a poem about themselves. Ask the children to point out the repeated words in the poem: 'When I was...' and 'That's what I could do'.

Poems about families: 1 and **2** (pages 85–86). This activity encourages the children to compare and contrast poems on a similar theme. They could find other lullabies to compare with these two. Talk about the opening lines of these two poems (the first two lines of 'Rock-a-bye, baby' and the 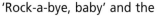 first three lines of 'Listen to the tree bear'). What kind of feeling does each poem have? Ask which words suggest this feeling. They should notice the comforting sound of the opening of 'Rock-a-bye, baby' and the frightened feeling of the opening of 'Listen to the tree bear'. Ask them about the change of feeling in each poem ('Rock-a-bye, baby' ends with a fright, but 'Listen to the tree bear' has a comforting ending).

Sorting poems (page 87). Before doing the activity, display and read with the children the poems mentioned on the sheet. Make them available during the activity so that the children can re-read them. Introduce the idea of grouping poems in themes: encourage the children to look for poems on a given theme (for example, food, school, families or toys and games) by asking them what a poem is about. They might think of additional themes for some of the poems they come across. The children could copy out or type out poems of their choice and illustrate them for a class anthology on a particular subject.

Learning objectives

The following chart shows how the Ages 5–6 activity sheets (pages 52–87) match the learning objectives addressed by the Year 1 units in the Poetry block of the Primary Framework for Literacy. (Where a page number is shown in bold type, this indicates the learning objective is the main focus of the activity.)

Objectives	Unit 1: Using the senses	Unit 2: Pattern and rhyme	Unit 3: Poems on a theme
Speaking			
Interpret a text by reading aloud with some variety in pace and emphasis	**52**, 53–57	59, **63**, 64, **65**, **66**, 68, **72**	**73**, **76**
Listening and responding			
Listen with sustained concentration, building new stores of words to communicate in different contexts	53, 55, 57, 58	59, 63, 64, 65, 66, 68	
Group discussion and interaction			
Ask and answer questions, make relevant contributions, offer suggestions and take turns	55, 56	63, 64, 72	85, 86
Explain their views to others in small groups	58	60, 61, 67	74, 75, 77, 78, 80, 82–84, 85
Word recognition: decoding (reading) and encoding (spelling)			
Recognise and use alternative ways of pronouncing the graphemes already taught	53	63, 64, 69	73–76, 79, 87
Recognise and use alternative ways of spelling the graphemes already taught	53	59–61, 63, **67**, **69**	74, 75, 79, 87
Identify the constituent parts of two- and three-syllable words to support application of phonic knowledge and skills	53, 57		74, 79, 85, 86, 87
Recognise automatically an increasing number of familiar high frequency words	52, 53, 55	59, 60, 64, 72	74, 75, 79, 87
Apply phonic knowledge and skills as the prime approach to reading and spelling unfamiliar words which are not completely decodable	52, 53, 56	59–69	73, 85, 86, 87

Objectives	Unit 1: Using the senses	Unit 2: Pattern and rhyme	Unit 3: Poems on a theme
Word recognition: decoding (reading) and encoding (spelling) *continued*			
Read more challenging texts which can be decoded using their acquired phonic knowledge and skills, along with automatic recognition of high frequency words	52, 53, 54, 57	59–61	73, 76, 77, 85, 86, 87
Read and spell phonically decodable two- and three-syllable words	52, 53, 56–58	59–63	78, **79**, 85, 86
Word structure and spelling			
Spell new words using phonics as the prime approach	58	68, 69	
Segment sounds into their constituent phonemes in order to spell them correctly	58	67, 68, 69	78, 79
Recognise and use alternative ways of spelling the graphemes already taught		67, 69	79
Use knowledge of common inflections in spelling, such as plurals, *-ly*, *-er*	58		79
Read and spell phonically decodable two- and three-syllable words	52, 58	59–62	78, 79
Understanding and interpreting texts			
Explain the effect of patterns of language and repeated words and phrases	52, **53, 54, 55, 57,** 58	**60, 61, 62,** 63, 64, 65, 66, 68, **71,** 72	73, **74, 75,** 76, 77, 78, 87
Engaging with and responding to texts			
Visualise and comment on events, characters and ideas, making imaginative links to own experiences	56, 57, **58**	62, 63, 64, 65, 66, 70, 71	73, **82, 85, 86, 87**
Creating and shaping texts			
Find and use new and interesting words and phrases, including 'story language'		**59,** 60, 61, 62, 63, **64,** 65, 66, **68,** 70, 71	74, 75, 77, **78, 80,** 81
Create short simple texts on paper and on screen which combine words with images (and sounds)	56	60, 61, 62, 63, 65, 66, 68, **70,** 71	**77, 81, 83, 84**

This finger's straight

• Say the rhyme.

This finger's straight;

This finger's curled;

This one's the tallest

In the world;

This finger stands

At the end of the line;

Here's a fat thumb

And I think it's mine.

Jack Ousbey

• Learn the rhyme.

 Look and read   **Cover**   **Say**   **Check**

• Say it to a friend.

Teachers' note Read the rhyme to the children, pointing to the appropriate fingers in turn; repeat it while they join in, pointing to their own fingers. As a further extension activity, the children could write and draw their own finger rhymes.

Developing Literacy Poetry Compendium: Ages 4–7 © A & C BLACK

Ride-a-cock-horse

• **Say the poem.**

Walk your fingers

along the hoof-prints.

Ride-a-cock-horse to Banbury Cross
To see a fine lady upon a white horse;
With rings on her fingers and bells on her toes,
She shall have music wherever she goes.

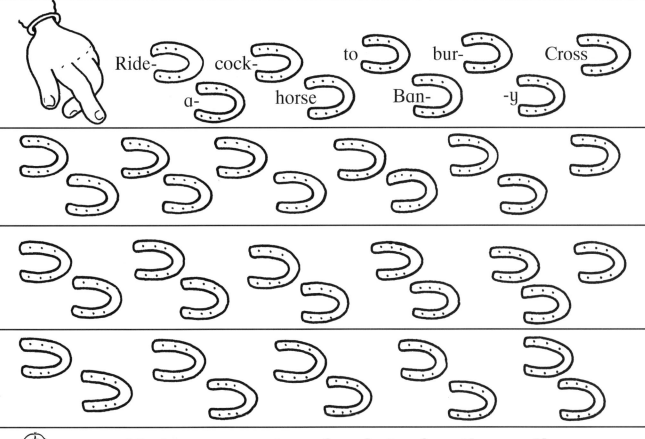

Ride-   cock-   to   bur-   Cross
a-   horse   Ban-   -y

Now try this!

• **Make some hoof-prints for these lines.**

To market, to market, to buy a fat pig.

Home again, home again, jiggety jig.

Teachers' note Read the poem aloud while the children follow the horse's hoof-prints by walking two fingers along them (if possible, first read it while they trot around the classroom or hall). The prints are in pairs to mimic the movement of a horse. The children could also 'trot' to other rhymes with a trotting rhythm.

Developing Literacy
Poetry Compendium:
Ages 4–7
© A & C BLACK

Point and read

- **Say the poem.**

Point to each word.

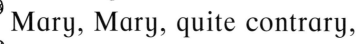

Mary, Mary, quite contrary,

How does your garden grow?

With silver bells and cockle shells

And pretty maids all in a row.

- **Join the words to the pictures.**

silver bells

cockle shells

pretty maids

garden

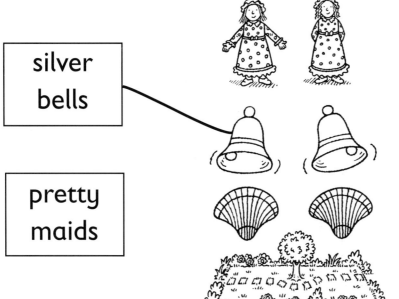

Now try this!

- **Find these words in the poem.**

Say the words.

pretty   contrary   cockle   quite

Teachers' note Display a large copy of the rhyme. Point to the words as you read, then invite some of the children, in turn, to point to the words while you read (the others check that they are right).

Developing Literacy
Poetry Compendium:
Ages 4–7
© A & C BLACK

Hair

- **Say the poem.**
  Clap to the rhythm.
- **Colour the lines of the poem:**

quick claps in [green]

slow claps in [yellow]

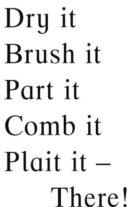

Hair

There's
Curly hair
Straight hair
Fine hair
Strong.
Black hair
Blonde hair
Short hair
Long.
Who cares
If my hair's
Every sort
Of wrong?
Hair!
Wash it
Dry it
Brush it
Part it
Comb it
Plait it –
There!

Dorothy Mills

Now try this!

- **Which five words did you say loudly?**

_____

Teachers' note Read the poem, placing emphasis on the stressed words: 'strong', 'long', 'wrong', 'hair', 'there'. The children could tap the rhythm on a table-top, stamp their feet or march around the room (ask them on which words they should stop). Point out the full stops and ask the children how they affect the way the poem is read.

Developing Literacy
Poetry Compendium:
Ages 4–7
© A & C BLACK

Eyes

- **Read the poem.**

  Fill in the gaps.

  ### Eyes

   There are

   _____ eyes

  _____ eyes

  _____ eyes

   Green.

   _____ eyes

  _____ eyes

  _____ eyes

   Mean.

  Think of colours.

  Think of the way eyes can look at you.

- **Write a verse about feet.**

   Now try this!

  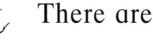 There are

  _____ feet

  _____ feet

  _____ feet

  _____ .

  Can you write another verse?

Teachers' note The children should first complete page 55. This simple format helps the children to structure their poems. You could also read the poem 'Wet' on page 57, which has a similar rhythm. The format could be used for other topics, such as food or toys. For the extension activity, brainstorm useful words: for example, thin, fat, short, long, heavy, light, running, stamping.

Developing Literacy Poetry Compendium: Ages 4–7
© A & C BLACK

Wet poem

- **Read the** list poem .

  Listen to the sounds.

- **Circle** Ⓡ **or** ⓡ **in** red

  Ⓢ **or** ⓢ **in** blue

Dark clouds,

Rain again,

Rivers on the

Misted pane.

Wet umbrellas

In the street,

Running noses,

Damp feet.

Shirley Hughes

- **Count:**

  How many Ⓡ **or** ⓡ **?** ☐

  How many Ⓢ **or** ⓢ **?** ☐

Now try this!

- **Read the poem again. Listen for other sounds which are the same.**
- **Write the letters.**

Teachers' note Introduce the activity by reading the poem to the children (emphasising the 'r' and 's' sounds) and asking them to listen to the sounds. Which sounds do they hear often? (r, s, ai, t, ee). Read the poem again, more slowly, and ask the children to listen to the beginnings of the words.

'Wet' from *Out and About* © 1988, 1998 Shirley Hughes

Developing Literacy Poetry Compendium: Ages 4–7 © A & C BLACK

Crazy creatures

<u>s</u>limy <u>s</u>nail

Listen to the sounds.

• **Write a word for each animal.**

Word-bank

buzzing
pink
red
wiggly

_____

worm

_____

robin

_____

bee

_____

pig

Now try this!

• **Write words for these.**

| bird | hen | fish |

Teachers' note With the children, read the words in the word-bank and the words for the animals, emphasising the initial consonants. Encourage them to repeat 'slimy snail' and to say what they notice about the sounds of the words. After they have completed the activity, ask the children to work in small groups to find other words for each animal and to say why they chose them.

Developing Literacy Poetry Compendium: Ages 4–7 © A & C BLACK

Picture jingle

- **Say the jingle.**
- **Draw a picture of it.**

Higglety, pigglety, pop!

The dog has eaten the mop;

The pig's in a hurry,

The cat's in a flurry,

Higglety, pigglety, pop!

- **Change the words of the jingle.**
- **Say your new jingle to a friend.**

Now try this!

Teachers' note Discuss jingles with the children: they are silly rhymes or songs which often have made-up words (such as those in advertisements). Can they think of other jingles? Give them some of the 'made-up words' as clues: for example, 'Diddle, diddle dumpling' and 'Hey, diddle, diddle'. The children should use pages 60 and 61 to complete the activity.

**Developing Literacy
Poetry Compendium:
Ages 4–7
© A & C BLACK**

Higglety, pigglety, pap!

Higglety, pigglety, par!

The cow's in the fountain,

The worm's in a muddle,

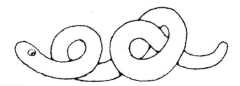

The snail is driving a car;

Higglety, pigglety, pap!

The pig's up a mountain,

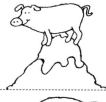

The fish is reading a map;

The rat's in a puddle,

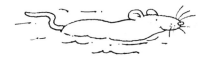

Higglety, pigglety, par!

Teachers' note The children should first complete the activity on page 59. Read the jingle again, asking them to notice which lines rhyme. Give a sample jingle for them to complete: for example, 'Higgledy, piggledy, poke! / The tiger's drinking —— (coke); / The lion's in the gutter, / The goat's in the —— (butter), / Higgledy, ——, ——. See also page 61.

Developing Literacy Poetry Compendium: Ages 4–7 © A & C BLACK

Jingle kit: 2

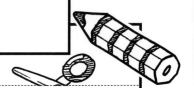

Higglety, pigglety, pike!

The snake is drinking tea;

The lion's on a rocket,

Higglety, pigglety, pea!

The bat is riding a bike;

The horse has got mittens,

The goat's in my pocket,

Higglety, pigglety, pea!

Higglety, pigglety, pike!

The seal has got kittens,

Teachers' note The children should first complete the activity on page 59. See also page 60. They should cut out the cards and discuss in small groups how to sort them to form jingles that rhyme. Ask them to explain their reasons for ordering them as they do. They could make up other jingles which follow the pattern of this one (see **Notes on the activities**, page 48).

Developing Literacy Poetry Compendium: Ages 4–7 © A & C BLACK

There I saw

- **Say the poem.**

- **Circle the words that** repeat .

I went up the high hill.

There I saw a climbing goat.

I went down by the running rill.

There I saw a ragged sheep.

I went under the green tree.

There I saw two doves asleep.

Anonymous

- **Make up your own poem.**

  Where did you go? What did you see?

I went _____

There I saw _____

I went _____

There I saw _____

Now try this!

- **Write four more lines for your poem.**

The lines do not have to rhyme.

Teachers' note Read the rhyme, drawing attention to the places mentioned by miming. Read the poem again and ask the children to match the places to the pictures. Can they work out what a rill is, from the words 'running rill'? The children can make up a poem, using this one as a pattern, about a familiar journey.

Developing Literacy Poetry Compendium: Ages 4–7 © A & C BLACK

Eat brown bread

- **Say the rhyme. Do the actions with your hands.**

A saveloy is a kind of sausage.

I-tiddly-i-ti,
Eat brown bread.

I saw a sausage
Fall down dead.

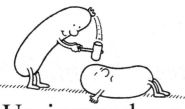

Up jumped a saveloy
And bopped him
on the head.

I-tiddly-i-ti,
Eat brown bread.

Now try this!

- **Say the rhyme to a friend.**

  Miss out the blank lines.

I-tiddly-i-ti,

▭ ▭ ▭ .

Your friend mimes the blank lines.

I saw a sausage

▭ ▭ ▭ .

Up jumped a saveloy

▭ ▭ ▭ ▭ ▭ ▭ .

I-tiddly-i-ti,

▭ ▭ ▭ .

Teachers' note Encourage the children to try reading this rhyme, using the pictures as cues to any new or difficult words. Emphasise that the actions are to be done with the hands only and that they should not touch their friend. In the extension activity, show them how to tap their hands in time to the rhythm of the missing lines while their friend mimes them.

Developing Literacy
Poetry Compendium:
Ages 4–7
© A & C BLACK

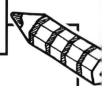

Eat fish and chips

• **Fill in the gaps.**

Word-bank

Wiggling his hips   fish and chips

kissed him on the lips

I-tiddly-i-ti,

Eat _fish_ _____ _____.

I saw a sausage

_____ _____ _____.

Up jumped a saveloy

And _____ _____ ____ _____ _____.

____ _____ ____ _____,

_____ _____ ____ _____.

• **Say the rhyme.**

Do the actions with

your hands.

> Point to the parts
> of your body.

Now try this!

• **Make up another rhyme using these.**

| some ghee | tapped him on the knee |

| In a tree |

Teachers' note The children should first complete the activity on page 63. They could learn the jingle before they begin this activity, by reading a line at a time, covering it, saying it and checking that they got it right.

Developing Literacy
Poetry Compendium:
Ages 4–7
© A & C BLACK

• **Read the song.**

Fill in the gaps.

Can you sing the song?

Deep in the forest in the middle of the night

I saw a lion who gave me a fright!

The _____ went "Grrr, grrr, grrr, _____, _____!"

And I went singing on my way.

Doo   doo   doobee   doobee   doo

Doo ___ _____ _____ ___

Doo ___ _____ _____ ___

And I went _____ ___ ___ ___.

Ian Sharp

Now try this !

• **Make up a verse about a wolf.**

Say or sing it with a friend.

Teachers' note Read (or sing) the forest song to the children and then repeat it with them joining in. Point out the chorus and introduce the word 'chorus'. Do they know any other poems or songs with choruses? See also page 66.

**Developing Literacy
Poetry Compendium:
Ages 4–7
© A & C BLACK**

65

- **Read the song.**

  Fill in the gaps.

Choose a different animal.

Deep in the forest in the middle of the night
I saw a _____ who gave me a fright!
The _____ went " _____, _____,

_____, _____, _____!"
And I went _____ ___ ___ ____.
Doo doo ___ ___ ___

___ ___ ___ ___ ___

___ ___ ___ ___ ___

And I went _____ ___ ___ ____.

- **Make up verses about these animals.**

  Take turns with a friend.

Now try this!

owl   cat   parrot   bee

Teachers' note The children should first complete the activity on page 65, to which they will need to refer while working on this activity. Revise the use of 'a' or 'an' before a noun and ask the children to notice which of the two they need for their chosen animal. During the plenary session, the children could sing their verses in the form of one long song.

Developing Literacy Poetry Compendium: Ages 4–7
© A & C BLACK

Far star

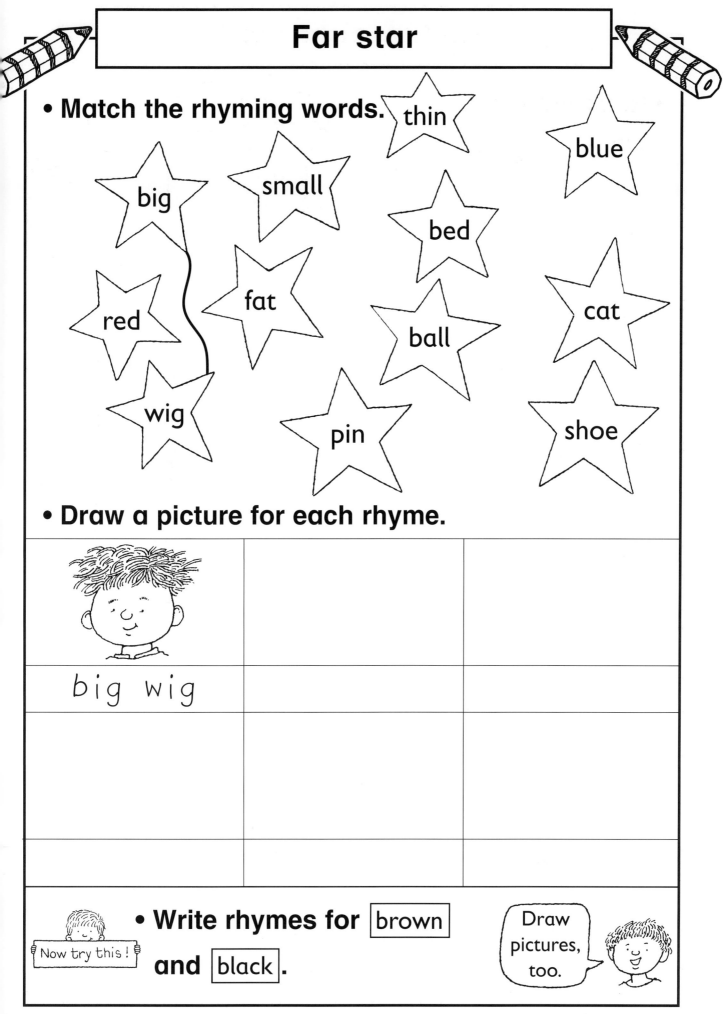

- **Match the rhyming words.**

thin

blue

big

small

bed

red

fat

cat

ball

wig

pin

shoe

- **Draw a picture for each rhyme.**

big wig

- **Write rhymes for** brown **and** black **.**

Now try this!

Draw pictures, too.

Teachers' note Introduce the activity by saying some rhyming descriptions: for example, 'long song', 'old gold', 'runny honey', 'third bird' and 'wide side'. After completing the activity, the children could work in pairs or small groups to think of others of their own. Ask them to explain why they chose their descriptions.

**Developing Literacy
Poetry Compendium:
Ages 4–7**
© A & C BLACK

67

Rub-a-dub-dub

- **Say the rhyme.**

Rub-a-dub-dub,

Three men in a tub.

Make new rhymes.

- **Fill in the gaps.**

Rot-a-tot-tot,

Three men in a _____.

Rug-a-d_____-d_____,

Three men in a _____.

R_____-a-d_____-d_____,

Three men in a _____.

- **Write rhymes for these.**

Draw pictures, too.

three men in a boat

three men on a phone

Teachers' note After reading the opening rhyme, ask the children to say which words rhyme. In the examples, they should predict the endings of the missing words (the pictures give clues). It may help if they are first given 'wrong' examples, such as 'Rot-a-tot-tot, Three men in a car' (ask what is wrong with it).

Developing Literacy
Poetry Compendium:
Ages 4–7
© A & C BLACK

The rhyme shop

Mrs Fun bought a bun. What did the others buy?

• **Write on the bags.**

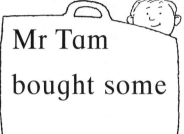

Mr Tam bought some _____.

Mrs Khan bought some _____.

Mr Gish bought some _____.

Rhyme shop

cake

dates

fish

naan

ham

ghee

Ms Lee bought some _____.

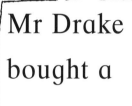

Mr Drake bought a _____.

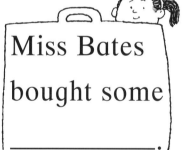

Miss Bates bought some _____.

• **What did these people buy?**

Now try this!

Mr Money _____   Mrs Head _____

Mrs Silk _____   Mr Tie _____

Miss Bear _____   Mr Dickens _____

Mr Price _____   Ms Kipps _____

Teachers' note Introduce the activity with a short list poem, for example: Mr Jones bought some bones; Mrs Biggs bought some figs; Ms Kaur bought some flour; Miss Raji bought a bhaji; Señora Gepetti bought some spaghetti. To help the children to make up their own rhymes, compile a foods word-bank.

Developing Literacy
Poetry Compendium:
Ages 4–7
© A & C BLACK

Pirates' shopping list

Pia and Paul are pirates.

- **Write their shopping list as a poem.**

Look at the pictures to help you.

Use a dictionary.

Pieces of eight

A talking parrot,
A wooden _____

_____

_____

_____

_____

_____

- **Draw and write four more things for the pirates' list.**

Now try this!

Teachers' note The children first need to have read and discussed some poems or stories about pirates and looked at pictures of them. Discuss words to describe the objects depicted: for example, golden, black, white, crossed, long, strong and sparkling. The long, narrow notebook format helps the children to structure the poem as a list.

**Developing Literacy
Poetry Compendium:
Ages 4–7**
© A & C BLACK

70

A week at the shops

- **Read the poem.**
- **Fill in the gaps.**

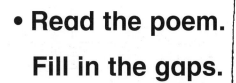

Monday	Tuesday	Wednesday
Thursday	Friday	Saturday

Hipperty hop to the corner shop

To buy some sweets for Sunday;

Some for you,

Some for me,

And some for sister Sandy.

Hipperty hop to the baker's shop

To buy some _____ for Monday;

Some for _____,

Some for _____,

And some for _____ _____.

Hipperty hop to the butcher's shop

To buy some _____ for _____;

Some for _____,

Some for _____,

And some for _____ _____.

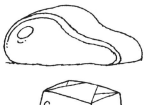

• **Write verses for these shops.**

Now try this!

| fishmonger's | grocer's | dairy | greengrocer's |

Teachers' note Read the first verse of the song with the children and model the second one. Although the words in the first verse alliterate, the children's words need not. They could replace 'sister Sandy' with another two-word name which has two syllables in each word and ends with 'y' for example, 'brother Andy', 'Auntie Mary'.

Developing Literacy
Poetry Compendium:
Ages 4–7
© A & C BLACK

71

Question and answer poem

- **Cut out the cards.**
- **Match the questions and answers.**
- **Say the poem.**

Work with a friend.

 Who goes there?

 To the market.

 Where are you going?

 A large round loaf.

 What will you buy?

 One pound twenty.

 What will it cost?

 An old friend.

 What will you bake?

 A bag of flour.

 Now try this!

- **Make up two more questions and answers for the poem.**

Teachers' note Introduce the activity by asking (or singing) a question, for example, 'What's your name?' and encouraging a child to say (or sing) an answer. In the extension activity, the children could sing their question to a partner, who could sing the answer, or they could draw and write it (the singing/response could then take place during the plenary session).

**Developing Literacy
Poetry Compendium:
Ages 4–7**
© A & C BLACK

One happy bear

- **Cut out the verses. Put them in order.**
- **Say the poem.**

One happy bear Dancing on the rocks. 	Six groaning ghosts Making mournful moans. 
Eight old elephants Flying to the moon. 	Four hairy trolls Sleeping in a cave. 
Ten green aphids Hiding underneath. 	Two shining stars Hidden in a box. 
Five skinny skeletons Rattling their bones. 	Seven booming drums beating out a tune. 
Nine red ladybirds Sitting on a leaf. 	Three billy goats Trying to be brave. 

Teachers' note After the children have cut out the verses of the poem and put them in order by reading the numbers, help them to read the whole poem, encouraging them to use the pictures as reading cues. Explain that ladybirds eat aphids. The poem could then be read around the class, with each group reading a verse in turn.

Developing Literacy
Poetry Compendium:
Ages 4–7
© A & C BLACK

Poem spinners: 1

Numbers

Four
4

Three
3

Five
5

Six
6

Two
2

One
1

Numbers

Ten
10

Eleven
11

Nine
9

Twelve
12

Eight
8

Seven
7

Objects

golden
ring

red
hen

blue
fish

rosy
apple

fluffy
cat

speckled
egg

Objects

old
shoe

cuddly
teddy

white
flower

silly
clown

tall
hat

wiggly
worm

Tip

Hold here to spin

Cap from ballpoint pen

Teachers' note The children should first complete the activity on page 73. Cut out the spinners and glue them on to card. Push the cap of a ballpoint pen through the centre, as shown. Working in pairs or small groups, the children spin a number, then an object and then a place. They read their verse: for example, 'Three magic wand(s) in the air'. Continued on page 75.

Developing Literacy Poetry Compendium: Ages 4–7 © A & C BLACK

Poem spinners: 2

Objects

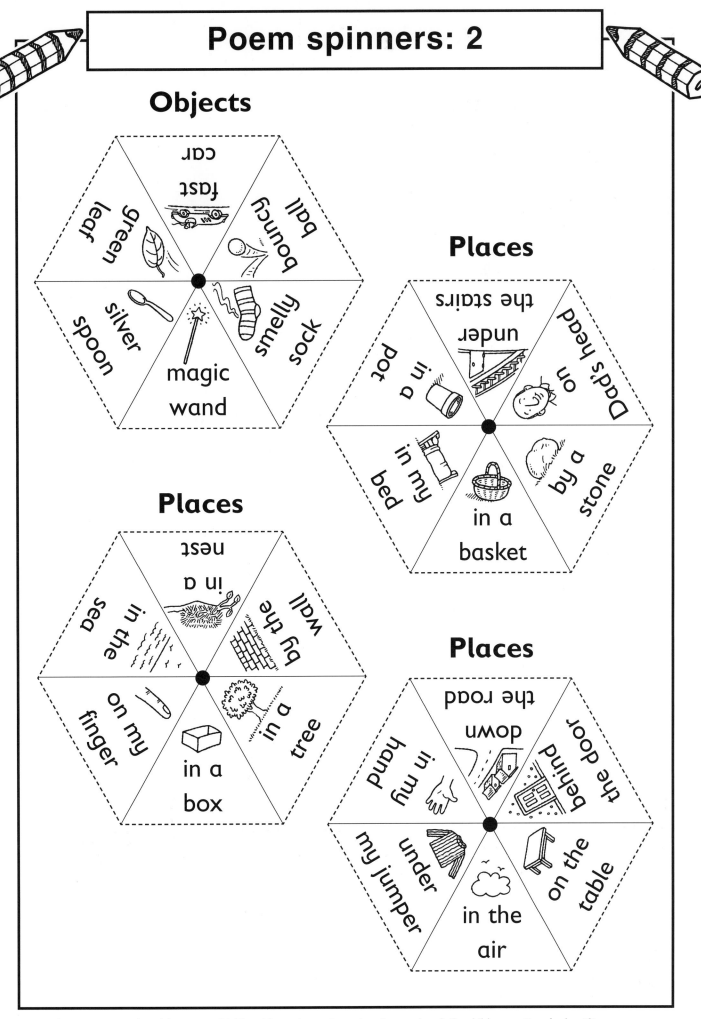

car
fast
bouncy
ball
green
leaf
smelly
sock
silver
spoon
magic
wand

Places

the stairs
under
Dad's head
on
in a
pot
by a
stone
in my
bed
in a
basket

Places

nest
in a
by the
wall
in the
sea
in a
tree
on my
finger
in a
box

Places

the road
down
behind
the door
in my
hand
on the
table
under
my jumper
in the
air

Teachers' note Continued from page 74. The object spinners have singular words; ask the children if they sound right and, if not, how they should change them and why. The children read aloud the verse they have 'spun'. They could repeat this several times and then draw and write their favourite verse. During the plenary session, the children could read their verses to the rest of the class.

Developing Literacy
Poetry Compendium:
Ages 4–7
© A & C BLACK

75

Ten fat sausages

- **Read the song.**
- **Circle the words that are numbers.**

Can you sing the song?

Ten fat sausages sizzling in the pan,

Ten fat sausages sizzling in the pan.

One went 'POP!' and the other went 'BANG!'

There were eight fat sausages

sizzling in the pan.

Eight fat sausages sizzling in the pan,

Eight fat sausages sizzling in the pan.

One went 'POP!' and the other went 'BANG!'

There were six fat sausages

sizzling in the pan.

Now try this!

What comes next?

- **Write the other verses.**
- **Sing the whole song.**

Teachers' note This song can be sung to the tune of *Ten green bottles*. The children could stand up to enact the song and jump in the air and call out 'pop' and 'bang'. Draw attention to the fact that the number of sausages is reduced by *two* in each verse. See also page 77.

Developing Literacy
Poetry Compendium:
Ages 4–7
© A & C BLACK

Countdown wheels

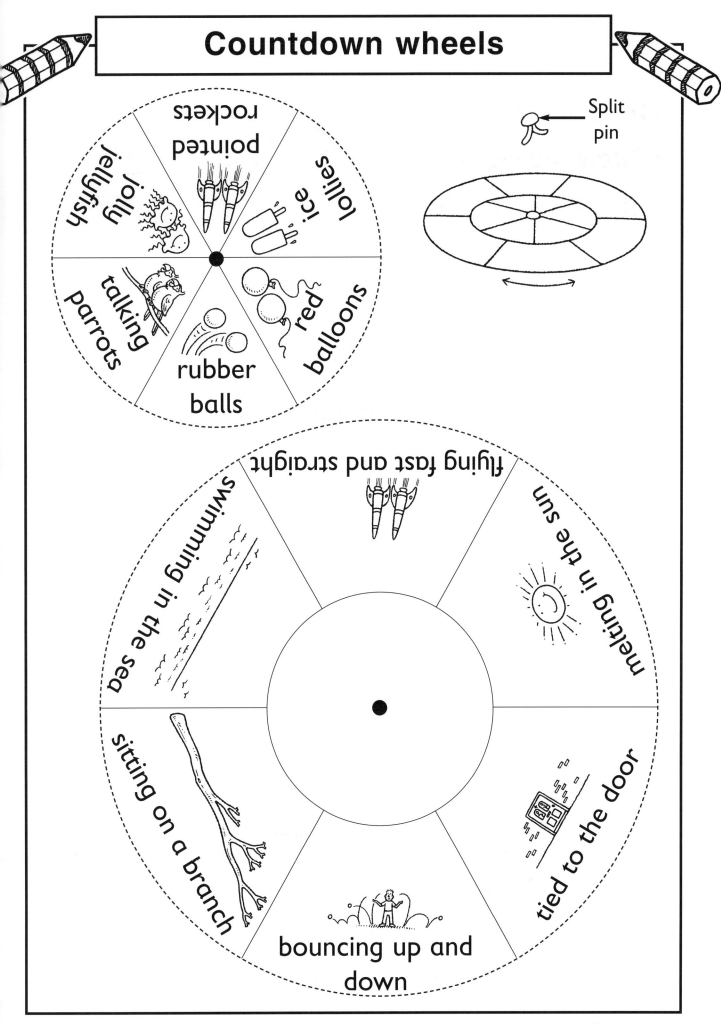

Split pin

jolly jellyfish

pointed rockets

ice lollies

talking parrots

red balloons

rubber balls

swimming in the sea

flying fast and straight

melting in the sun

sitting on a branch

tied to the door

bouncing up and down

Teachers' note The children should first complete the activity on page 76. Copy the page onto card, cut out the wheels and fasten them as shown. The children choose an item from the smaller wheel and turn the wheel until they find an action which is a suitable match. They make up a 'countdown' rhyme modelled on *Ten fat sausages*. In small groups, brainstorm ideas for sounds for each item.

Developing Literacy
Poetry Compendium:
Ages 4–7
© A & C BLACK

Zany zoo

• **Say the names of the animals.**

Ⓛena ⓵adybird   Ⓣom ⓽iger   Ⓓilly ⓓuck

• **Make up names for these animals.**

Make the first sounds the same.

_____ bee   _____ lion   _____ monkey

_____ ant   _____ snake   _____ giraffe

• **Make up names for six other animals.**

• **Draw the animals.**

Teachers' note The children should first read aloud the names of the animals at the top of the page. Ask them what they notice about the names. Can they think up other names for the same animals? What rule do they need to follow? Ask them to work in pairs or small groups to make up names for the other animals and to explain their choices.

Developing Literacy
Poetry Compendium:
Ages 4–7
© A & C BLACK

Weather words

- **Say the words.**

- **Match the first sounds.**

Listen to the first sounds.

foggy   slope

hard   field

cold   weather

misty   day

slippery   hailstones

wet   corner

damp   morning

Now try this!

- **Make up pairs of words about today's weather. Make the first sounds the same.**

Teachers' note Read some alliterative descriptions of weather to the children and ask them what they notice about the sounds of the words: for example, 'warm wind', 'silent snow'. In the extension activity, encourage the children first to think of any words about weather and then to look for alliterative pairs (this could be done as a guided writing activity).

Developing Literacy
Poetry Compendium:
Ages 4–7
© A & C BLACK

List poem notebook

- **Write some words about today's weather.**

Use a dictionary.

Now try this!

- **Write some words about how today's weather makes you feel.**

Teachers' note Re-read the poem 'Wet' (page 57) as an example of a list poem, talk about the weather vocabulary in it and compile a weather word-bank. Introduce the idea of a notebook for collecting ideas for poems. The children could discuss today's weather in pairs or small groups and explain to each other how it makes them feel.

Developing Literacy Poetry Compendium: Ages 4–7 © A & C BLACK

List poem

• **Draw and write a list poem.**

Title _____

	_____
	_____
	_____
	_____
	_____
	_____
	_____

• **Say your poem.**

• **Mark anything you want to change.**

• **Re-draft your poem.**

Teachers' note Use this blank format to help the children to structure a list poem on any topic. If they choose the topic of the weather, it would be helpful to have completed pages 79–80. After reading their poems aloud, the children might be able to decide how to change the rhythm (for example, by reducing some lines to just one word). This could be done as a guided writing activity.

**Developing Literacy
Poetry Compendium:
Ages 4–7
© A & C BLACK**

When I was... 1

When I was born
I could cry.
That's what I could do.

What could you do at different ages?

- **Write a poem. Start with** When I was .

Use the words and pictures to help you.

Picture	Picture	Number	Word
cry	sleep	0	born
walk	talk	1	one
hop	skip	2	two
kick	read	3	three
		4	four
		5	five
		6	six

Teachers' note Talk to the children about what they could do at different ages and what they can do now. Record their responses, which can be used to support work on pages 83–84. Ask them how old they are now and how this will change the words they write: for example, 'Now I am — I can —.'

Developing Literacy
Poetry Compendium:
Ages 4–7
© A & C BLACK

When I was... 2

When I was _____
I could _____.
That's what I could do.

When I was _____

_____

_____

_____

When I was _____

_____

_____

_____

Teachers' note The children should first complete the activity on page 82. On each strip, they draw a picture and write a line about what they could do at each age. Cut out the strips and staple them, with those on page 84, to make a booklet (copy an extra strip for children who are six). The children could make a cover and write the title, 'When I was…' See also page 84.

Developing Literacy
Poetry Compendium:
Ages 4–7
© A & C BLACK

83

When I was _____

I could _____.

That's what I could do.

_____

_____

_____

_____

Now I am _____

I can _____.

That's what I can do.

Teachers' note Continued from page 83. Remind the children of the differences between writing about their age now and their age in the past (am/was, can/could). When they have completed both pages, they could read what they have written as a poem. Ask them to explain to a partner or to their group why they chose the activities in their poem.

Developing Literacy Poetry Compendium: Ages 4–7
© A & C BLACK

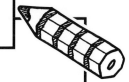

Rock-a-bye, baby

Rock-a-bye, baby, on the tree-top,
When the wind blows the cradle will rock;
When the bough breaks the cradle will fall,
Down will come baby, cradle and all.

Listen to the tree bear

Listen to the tree bear
Crying in the night
Crying for his mammy
In the pale moonlight.

What will his mammy do?
When she hears him cry?
She'll tuck him in a cocoa-pod
And sing a lullaby.

Teachers' note Read the two poems with the children. Ask them what is similar about the poems and what is different? They could cut out the poem outlines and glue them into their own anthology. Which lullaby do they find the more comforting? Ask them to discuss with a partner or in small groups why they found it comforting. See also page 86.

Developing Literacy
Poetry Compendium:
Ages 4–7
© A & C BLACK

Poems about families: 2

● Colour the correct answers.

Rock-a-bye, baby

What kind of family?	human	animal
Who is in the poem?	baby	grandpa
	father	mother
Happy or sad beginning?	happy	sad
Happy or sad ending?	happy	sad

Listen to the tree bear

human	animal
baby	grandpa
father	mother
happy	sad
happy	sad

● **Which poem do you like better?** _____

● **Why?** _____

Teachers' note The children first need to have read the poems on page 85, and they will require copies of these poems for reference. Some children will need help in reading the questions.

Developing Literacy
Poetry Compendium:
Ages 4–7
© A & C BLACK

Sorting poems

• **Cut out the cards. Sort the poems.**

Poems about animals	Poems about food	Poems about school	Poems about toys and games

 Eat brown bread

 Mary had a little lamb

 Jack Sprat

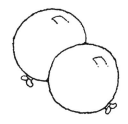 Balloons... balloons

 Two little dogs

 Jelly on a plate

 Jumping Joan

 Alphabet song

 First day at school

 The snail

Teachers' note The children need not have read the poems. Discuss the titles and pictures and ask what they think the poems are about. The children could glue the titles onto a large sheet of paper beneath the four headings. As an extension activity, they could add more poems to each set. They might find some which do not fit into these sets; ask them to make up new headings.

**Developing Literacy
Poetry Compendium:
Ages 4–7
© A & C BLACK**

Notes on the activities

The notes below expand upon those provided at the bottom of the activity pages. They give ideas and suggestions for making the most of the activity sheet, including suggestions for the whole-class introduction, the plenary session or for follow-up work using an adapted version of the sheet. The activities are grouped into units in line with the Primary Framework for Literacy, but the pages need not be presented in the order in which they appear, unless stated otherwise.

Many of the activities suggest that the children memorise a poem, rhyme or verse. To help them in this, read it aloud and then repeat it, encouraging them to join in. Either display an enlarged copy of the poem, or work with a small group of children who each have their own copy to follow. Read a line, then cover it and ask the children to repeat the line, gradually building up the number of lines covered, until the children can recite the entire poem. The following mnemonic appears in several activities to remind the children how they can learn a poem:

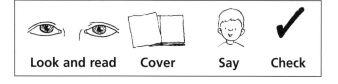

| Look and read | Cover | Say | Check |

Unit 1: Patterns on the page

In this section the children respond to and write poems with particular patterns and structures, created both by the ways in which words and phrases are used and by the way the text is laid out on the page. The poems should be read aloud by the children, either taking turns during the introductory session or in groups; give them opportunities to experiment with different ways of reading the poems aloud (including different numbers of voices for different parts of the poem), and encourage them to look out for repeated parts, such as choruses, which could be read by the whole group.

The witches' spell: 1 and **2** (pages 93–94). The extract on page 93 is a poem for the children to listen to and recognise the evil atmosphere, and then to read for themselves. They could take turns to read a line aloud, making it sound like the witches' spell it is, with the whole class joining in the chorus. Tell the children that Macbeth met three witches who used their magic to foretell his future. Explain the meanings of any difficult words ('fenny' means 'from a marsh or bog')

and ask them to name some of the horrible things in the spell. On page 94, the children use 'ingredients' from the word-bank to complete the First Witch's spell.

Pattern poem (page 95). During the plenary session the children could take turns around the class to read a line from their poems. They could decide which lines could be combined to make a class poem to be written up and illustrated for display or written in a book for younger children in the school (using a computer to save time in writing the repeated lines).

Chat poem (page 96). Read (or sing) the lines of the following traditional rhyme, stopping at the asterisks for the children to try to supply the missing words:

See you later, *alligator. / In a while, *crocodile. / See you later, hot *potato. / If you wish, *jellyfish.

This can be linked with work on rhyme, since rhyme is often part of the pattern of a poem. It could also be linked with work on the different spellings of similar sounds (for example, week/freak).

The way you say it: 1 and **2** (pages 97–98). The counting poem on page 97 should be read aloud with a 'counting' rhythm. Ask the children to notice where the pauses are. How do the pauses help them to count? Can they work out how the numbers between 11 and 19 are formed? Some children might also be able to work out the names for 21 to 29 and invent a word for 30. On page 98 the children make up their own words for numbers. During the plenary session, ask them to explain how they chose the words.

Aliens' alphabet (page 99). The children should first write out and recite the normal English alphabet, noticing which letters rhyme (a, j, k and b, c, d, e, g, p, t, v). Encourage the children to try to make the corresponding letters in the aliens' alphabet rhyme; they could also make the names for them begin with the same sounds as their corresponding letters in the English alphabet (for example, ag, bag, cag, dag, eag). Ask them to recite their alphabets.

The drum (page 100). This poem has the rhythm of heartbeats, making the drum seem to be a living thing. The children could identify the words and phrases which contribute to this effect ('skin', 'belly', 'a living heart', 'a living goat', 'a living tree'). One group could read the poem aloud while another beats drums quietly in a regular beat. The children could find out about the rhythm of a heart beating by listening to one another's heartbeats through stethoscopes (or rubber tubing with funnels on the ends).

Rhyme match: 1 and **2** (pages 101–102). These activities are based on the traditional skipping rhyme:

> Up and down, up and down,
> All the way to London Town.
> Heel and toe, heel and toe,
> All the way to Jericho.
> Swish swash, swish swash,
> All the way to Charing Cross.

The last two lines have been changed to avoid half-rhymes, but these could be introduced to children who are ready for them. Some children might be able to make up their own verses.

Party poppers (page 103). The children could first make notes about parties: for example, games, foods, activities and things to wear, as well as descriptions of the atmosphere and what happens. They could take turns around the class to add an alliterative noun to a descriptive word: for example, 'moaning Mum', 'grinning Granddad', 'crunching crisps', 'soggy sandwiches', 'funny faces', 'hilarious hats'.

Unit 2: Really looking

This section focuses on poems based on closely observed experience. Encourage the children to imagine themselves in the situation of the writer of the poem and to discuss the feelings evoked by the poem. They should think about the way the writer has chosen and used words to describe the details of his or her experience or observation.

The horseman (page 104). This is a poem for the children to read aloud and to memorise. They should notice the rhyming words. In the first two lines, point out the words which begin with the same sound: 'heard', 'horseman' and 'hill'. Talk about the atmosphere of the poem and ask the children what kind of picture it makes them imagine (the weather, the air, the light and shade and the colours). They could paint or draw these pictures.

Word-pictures: 1 and **2** (pages 105–106). To develop the children's appreciation of the ways in which poets can create pictures using a few well-chosen words, display poems and draw attention to evocative lines or groups of words. The words could be copied and displayed in enlarged form. Examples include: 'homewards plods his weary way' ('Elegy Written in a Country Churchyard', Thomas Gray), 'yellow-brown slackness soft bellied' ('Snake', D. H. Lawrence), 'No stir in the air, no stir in the sea' ('The Inchcape Rock', Robert Southey). Discuss the images which the words conjure up and encourage the children to describe and draw these images. The extracts on page 105 are from 'The Listeners' (Walter de la Mare), 'Shining Things' (Elizabeth Gould), 'I Saw' (Anon) and 'My Sari'

(Debjanee Chatterjee). Page 106 helps the children to create their own 'word-pictures', by providing a structure on which they can make notes about their observations, write a description based on their notes, highlight the most important words and then write a short 'word-picture'.

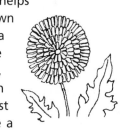

Sad sounds, happy sounds (page 107). This helps to develop the children's appreciation of the ways in which poets create effects to convey feelings. The extracts are from: 'Ode to a Nightingale' (John Keats), 'Everyone Sang' (Siegfried Sassoon), 'Come on into my Tropical Garden' (Grace Nichols), 'Farewell Address' (Chief Plenty Coups, leader of the Crow people) and 'Daffodils' (William Wordsworth).

Sad words, happy words (page 108). This activity develops the children's skills in making and organising notes and jottings to use in their own poems. Encourage them to look for sad and happy words in other poems. They could also look for gentle and powerful words.

Poets' words (page 109). You could introduce this page through the poems of Lewis Carroll (who invented 'slithy') or Edward Lear (who invented 'runcible spoon'), as well as those of modern poets like Colin West (who invented the phrase 'at a total lossage' to describe his feelings when trying to find a rhyme for 'sausage'!).

Your own words (page 110). This helps the children to invent their own words. Before this activity is presented, a 'word-factory' could be set up in the classroom – a table and display area containing materials to stimulate the creation of new words: for example, illustrated examples of made-up words (like those on the activity sheet) and words invented by writers of stories and poems, along with old words which are no longer used (such as ones coined by Shakespeare).

Green poem and **Red poem** (pages 111–112). Before the lesson, the children could keep notebooks in which to make jottings about anything they see which is green (or red). They could take turns to name green things: 'Green leaves, green string, green buds,' and so on (or red things: 'Red car, red ball, red shoes,' and so on).

Hump, jump, wiggle, jiggle and **Crash, dash, rumble, tumble** (pages 113–114). These encourage the children to look for rhymes that make sense: they consider the ways in which the animals move, find the right words for these movements and then arrange them in rhyming pairs. This can be linked with work on vocabulary extension (interesting words for movement to replace 'go'/'goes' and 'went') and with phonological awareness (initial sounds, medial phonemes and word endings).

Rats! (page 115). This activity develops the children's ability to recognise the ways in which poets create particular effects by their choice of words. In this instance, several devices are combined, but the focus is on alliteration. Ask the children what sort of picture the poem creates in their minds. They could draw or paint the picture they imagine. Ask them what gives this 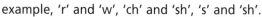 impression: they might notice that many activities of the rats are described in just a few lines. The scuttling and rushing of the rats are emphasised by the repetition throughout the verse of 's' sounds.

Anthology: the sea (page 116). This provides a format on which the children can collect an anthology of evocative lines from poems about the sea. Encourage them to look for lines which they enjoy reading or which conjure up pictures or ideas they like.

A poet (page 117) provides a structure to help the children to think about specific aspects of the work of a significant children's poet.

Unit 3: Silly stuff

Here the children are encouraged to laugh: to enjoy nonsense poems, poems which explore words and ideas, and to play tricks with tongue-twisters and riddles. They also think about the way the poet has achieved his or her humorous effects.

One weird week (page 118). The children should notice the repeated 's' sounds of the first line. Ask them which sound should be repeated in each of the other lines. This can be linked with work on extending vocabulary (the calendar) and on phonemes and initial consonants.

Nonsense poems (page 119). This presents a poem written purely for fun. The activity provides the children with a structure for a nonsense poem in the style of the example on the page. Draw attention to the details about real birds which are included (feathers and nest). Provide pictures of fish and discuss what they look like and what they do (and what they *don't* do), where they live (and where they *don't* live). With the children, compile a word-bank.

Freeze, froze, sneeze, snooze (page 120). This could be linked with sentence structure work on the construction of past tenses. The children could look for patterns in the formation of past tenses and find any

which do not fit the patterns: for example: grow/grew, know/knew (but not glow/glew); ring/rang, sing/sang (but not bring/brang or fling/flang).

Ask a silly question (page 121). This begins with an example from an anonymous poem. Read it to the children:

> The man in the wilderness
>   Asked of me
> How many strawberries
>   Grew in the sea.
>
> I answered him
>   As I thought good,
> As many as herrings
>   Grew in the wood.

Riddle match (page 122). This develops the children's ability to look at things from different points of view. Some of them might be able to think of riddles based on dual meanings of words: for example, tongue (of a person or a shoe) and eye (of a person or a needle). A class collection of riddles could be compiled, perhaps using a computer, to be published for the enjoyment of others in the school. *Answers*: 1A, 2D, 3F, 4B, 5C, 6E. The answer to the riddle in the extension activity is: your reflection.

Riddle-me-ree (page 123). Here the children need to look closely at the spellings of words in order to identify the letter of the clue. This could be linked with work on phonemes, letter combinations and spelling strategies and rules. *Answers*: t, a , b, l, e: TABLE.

Riddle writer (page 124). This page provides a structure to help the children to write riddles.

Tongue-twister kit: 1 and **2** and **Twister writer** (pages 125–127). These could be linked with work on alliterative patterns, but the essential difference between the two should be pointed out: poets use alliteration to create effects and feelings whereas tongue-twisters are mainly for fun. Ask the children which tongue-twisters they find the most difficult to say quickly, and discuss which phonemes are difficult to say when they follow one another closely: for example, 'r' and 'w', 'ch' and 'sh', 's' and 'sh'.

Word-juggler jokes (page 128). This presents the kinds of joke which children tell one another. *Answers*:
1. Be quiet while I'm spooking.
2. Up his sleevies!
3. Tweethearts!
Mount Cleverest, The Ghost Office, Oinkment, Stable tennis

Learning objectives

The following chart shows how the Ages 6–7 activity sheets (pages 93–128) match the learning objectives addressed by the Year 2 units in the Poetry block of the Primary Framework for Literacy. (Where a page number is shown in bold type, this indicates the learning objective is the main focus of the activity.)

Objectives	Unit 1: Patterns on the page	Unit 2: Really looking	Unit 3: Silly stuff
Speaking			
Speak with clarity and use appropriate intonation when reading and reciting texts	**93**, 97, 98, 100–102	**104**, 113, 115	118, 120, 121
Group discussion and interaction			
Listen to each other's views and preferences, agree the next steps to take and identify contributions by each group member	96, 97		
Word recognition: decoding (reading) and encoding (spelling)			
Read independently and with increasing fluency longer and less familiar texts	93, 96, 97	104, 113, 115, **116**	
Spell with increasing accuracy and confidence, drawing on word recognition and knowledge of word structure and spelling patterns	95, 96, 98, 99, 103	117	118–120, 124, 127, 128
Know how to tackle unfamiliar words which are not completely decodable	93, 95–97, 101–103	107–109	120–122, 125–128
Read and spell less common alternative graphemes including trigraphs	93, 95, 96, 102	105, 107–109, 116	118–121, 125–127
Read high and medium frequency words independently and automatically	93, 95, 96, 100–103	104, 105, 107–109, 113, 114, 116	118–126, 128
Word structure and spelling			
Spell with increasing accuracy and confidence, drawing on word recognition and knowledge of word structure, and spelling patterns including common inflections and use of double letters	95–99, 103		120, 121, 124, 125, 127
Read and spell less common alternative graphemes including trigraphs	93, 95, 96, 102	105, 107–109, 116	118–121, 125–127

Objectives	Unit 1: Patterns on the page	Unit 2: Really looking	Unit 3: Silly stuff
Understanding and interpreting texts			
Explore how particular words are used, including words and expressions with similar meanings	93, 96, **97**, 99, **101**, **102**	104, **105**, **107**, **108**, **109**, 110, **111**, 112, **113**, 114, **115**, 116	118, 120–122, **123**, **125**, **126**, 127, 128
Engaging with and responding to texts			
Explain their reactions to texts, commenting on important aspects	97, 98, **100**	104, 105, 107, 113, 116, **117**	122, 123, 125, 126
Creating and shaping texts			
Draw on knowledge and experience of texts in deciding and planning what and how to write	**94**, **95**, **96**, 98, 99, 103	106, 110–112, 117	118, **119**, 121–123, **124**, 127, **128**
Make adventurous word and language choices appropriate to style and purpose of text	94, 95, **98**, **99**, **103**	**106**, **110**, 111, **112**, **114**	**118**, 119, **120**, **121**, **122**, 123, 124, **127**, 128
Select from different presentational features to suit particular writing purposes on paper and on screen	103	117	121
Presentation			
Write legibly, using upper and lower case letters appropriately within words, and observing correct spacing within and between words	94–99	105–108, 110–114, 116, 117	118–121, 123, 124, 127, 128
Form and use the four basic handwriting joins	94–99	105–108, 110–114, 116, 117	118–121, 123, 124, 127, 128
Word-process short narrative and non-narrative texts	103	110	124, 127

The witches' spell: 1

• **Say the witches' spell.**

This is from a play called *Macbeth* by William Shakespeare. There were three witches.

All Double, double toil and trouble;

Fire burn, and cauldron bubble.

Second Witch Fillet of a fenny snake,

In the cauldron boil and bake;

Eye of newt and toe of frog,

Wool of bat and tongue of dog,

Adder's fork and blind-worm's sting,

Lizard's leg and owlet's wing,

For a charm of powerful trouble,

Like a hell-broth boil and bubble.

All Double, double toil and trouble;

Fire burn, and cauldron bubble.

Teachers' note The poem could be read aloud two or three times, with groups taking turns to read the words of the Second Witch and the whole class reading the words spoken in chorus by all three witches.

Developing Literacy Poetry Compendium: Ages 4–7 © A & C BLACK

Word-bank

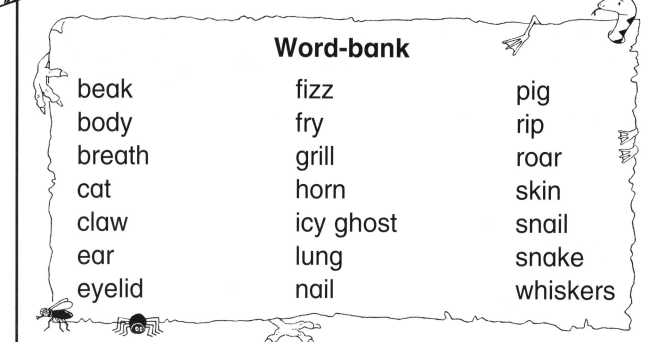

beak	fizz	pig
body	fry	rip
breath	grill	roar
cat	horn	skin
claw	icy ghost	snail
ear	lung	snake
eyelid	nail	whiskers

• **Write a spell for the First Witch. Fill in the gaps.**

First Witch

<u>Body</u> of a blue-black fly,

In the cauldron roast and _____;

Slime of _____ and _____ of goat,

Skin of _____ and _____ of stoat,

Vulture's _____ and weasel's _____,

Beetle's _____ and lion's _____,

For a charm of powerful trouble,

Like a hell-broth boil and bubble.

Now try this!

• **List some things for the Third Witch's spell. Use the word-bank to help you.**

Think of horrible things.

Teachers' note The children should first complete the activity on page 93. Encourage them to re-read the witches' spell from *Macbeth* while completing this page, to help them to decide where the rhymes should be and to match their own 'spells' to the rhythm of the original. Their spells need not rhyme.

Developing Literacy Poetry Compendium: Ages 4–7
© A & C BLACK

Pattern poem

- **Fill in the gaps in the poem.**
- **Draw a picture for the last verse.**

Notice the pattern of the poem.

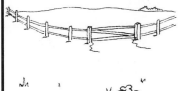
This is Farmer Fran's field.

This is the grass which grew in Farmer Fran's field.

This is the cow which ate the grass which _____ _____ _____

_____ _____.

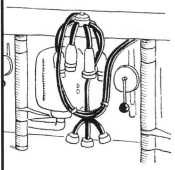
This is the machine which milked the cow which _____

_____

_____.

This is _____

_____

_____

_____

_____.

Now try this!

- **Write another** pattern poem .
  You can begin with any of these.

| This is Sean's shed | This is Clare's car | This is Tom's toy box |

Teachers' note The children could first read the nursery rhyme 'The House that Jack Built' so that they can model their poems on it. They should notice that each verse begins by introducing something new and then linking it to the thing introduced in the previous verse. Some children might be able to continue the poem on another sheet of paper.

Developing Literacy
Poetry Compendium:
Ages 4–7
© A & C BLACK

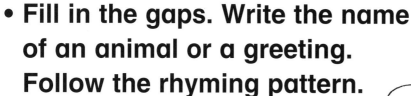

Chat poem

- **Fill in the gaps. Write the name of an animal or a greeting. Follow the rhyming pattern.**

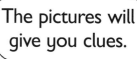
The pictures will give you clues.

Animal Chat

"See you later, alligator."

"In a while, <u>crocodile</u>."

"Hello, _____."

"_____, butterfly."

"Take care, _____."

"_____, blue jay."

"Bye for now, brown _____."

"How do you do, _____?"

"Hi, _____."

"Good luck, little _____."

buffalo

kangaroo

crocodile

polar bear

cow

fly

duck

- **Make up an animal chat poem using these.**

| Of course | That's nice | Cheerio |

Teachers' note Begin by reciting some of the words of the song 'See You Later, Alligator' (see **Notes on the activities**, page 88). Ask the children to think of words and phrases which people often use in conversation: for example, 'Hello,' and 'Bye for now'. Can they think of animals' names which rhyme with them? The children can take turns to recite the completed lines to a partner.

**Developing Literacy
Poetry Compendium:
Ages 4–7**
© A & C BLACK

**Counting sheep can be boring!
Some shepherds have made up their
own numbers, for fun.**

- **Read this shepherds'** counting poem .

Yan, tan, tether, mether, pimp.

Sether, hether, hother, dother, dick.

Yan dick, tan dick, tether dick,

mether dick, bumfit.

Yan bumfit, tan bumfit, tether

bumfit, mether bumfit, gigot.

Anonymous

- **Make up words to fill the gaps.**

Eeg, teeg, teeger, _____, _____.

Saggle, _____, _____, _____, tag.

Eeg tag, _____ tag, _____ tag, _____ _____,

tackit.

Eeg tackit, _____ tackit, _____ _____,

_____ _____, _____.

Now try this!

- **Write another counting poem using
numbers you have made up.**

Teachers' note Make an enlarged copy of the poem only. Invite children in turn to read it while
the others listen. Then ask them to read it as if the words were numbers. What difference do the
others notice? Read out lists of words, including series of numbers in other languages, using a
'counting' rhythm for some but not others. See if the children can say when you are 'counting'.

**Developing Literacy
Poetry Compendium:
Ages 4–7
© A & C BLACK**

Any words can sound like numbers if you say them as if you are counting.

- **Say these words.**

Try to sound as if you are counting.

> Walk, talk, think, fall, find.
>
> Sing, settle, aim, nod, take.

- **Fill in the gaps.**
- **Say the words as if you are counting.**

These are words for foods.

Jam, tea, _____, _____, _____.
_____, sausage, _____, _____, _____.

These are parts of the body.

Leg, toe, _____, _____, _____.
_____, ankle, _____, _____, _____.

These are colours.

Red, blue, _____, _____, _____.
_____, _____, _____, _____, _____.

Now try this!

How can you make higher numbers?

You could add a word to each 'number'.

- **Write the next two lines for each person.**

Teachers' note The children should first complete the activity on page 97. Read the counting poem again, asking them to notice how many 'numbers' there are in each line. The children should think about how many syllables there are in each 'number'. With a partner, they can read aloud the lines they have written. Do they sound as if they are counting?

Developing Literacy Poetry Compendium: Ages 4–7
© A & C BLACK

Aliens' alphabet

- **Make up names for the missing letters in the aliens' alphabet.**

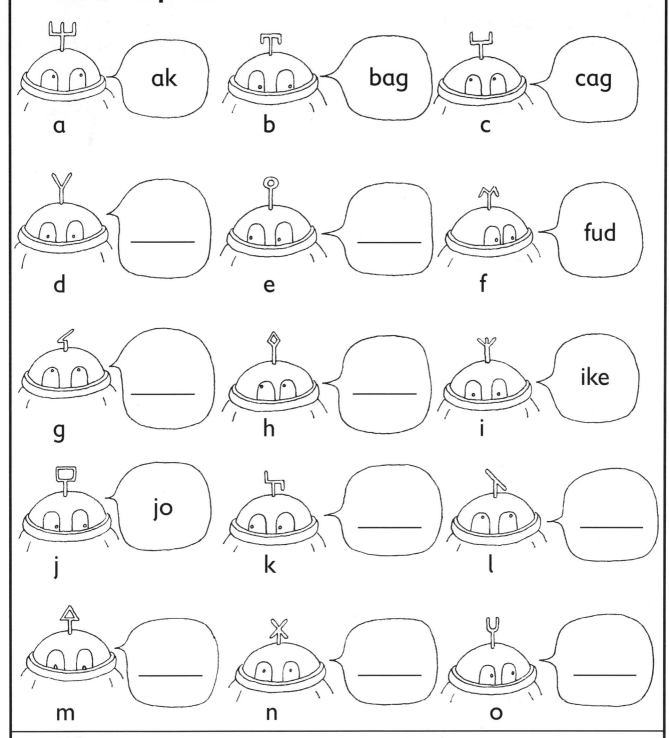

- **Write the rest of the aliens' alphabet.**
- **Say it aloud.**

Teachers' note The children should make up letter names which have the same number of syllables ('beats') as the letters of the alphabet. Ask them which is the only letter with more than one syllable (w). Some children might be able to continue the aliens' alphabet so that the letters rhyme in the same sequence as the real alphabet.

Developing Literacy Poetry Compendium: Ages 4–7 © A & C BLACK

The drum

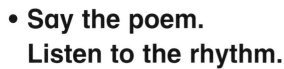

- **Say the poem.**
  Listen to the rhythm.
- **Draw a cross ⊠ above each** ⬚beat⬚ **.**

Some words might have two beats.

De Beat

X   X   X   X
De beat of de drum
    is a living heart

De skin of de drum
    is a living goat

De wood of de drum
    is a living tree

De belly of de drum
    is de call of de sea

De dum of de drum is me

Grace Nichols

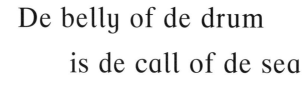

- **Say the poem while your friend beats a drum.**
- **Check that the crosses are right.**

Take turns as readers and drummers.

Teachers' note Read the poem aloud, then re-read it with the children quietly beating drums, tapping tambourines or tapping their knees or the table-tops. Ask them how the words 'de drum' and 'de beat' help to create the rhythm of the poem. What difference would it make if they were changed to 'the beat' and 'the drum'?

Developing Literacy Poetry Compendium: Ages 4–7
© A & C BLACK

 Up and down,

up and down,

 Heel and toe,

heel and toe,

 Tap your knee,

tap your knee,

 Clap your hands,

clap your hands,

 Hoppety hop,

hoppety hop,

 Crissy cross,

crissy cross,

 Spin around,

spin around,

 Left and right,

left and right,

 Out and in,

out and in,

 Shake a leg,

shake a leg,

 Sing a song,

sing a song,

 Dance a jig,

dance a jig,

Teachers' note Introduce some of the rhyming pairs as a skipping rhyme: 'Up and down, up and down, / All the way to London town. Heel and toe, heel and toe, / All the way to Jericho'. Two children could turn a rope while another skips and does the actions (see **Notes on the activities**, page 89). Continued on page 102.

Developing Literacy Poetry Compendium: Ages 4–7 © A & C BLACK

Rhyme match: 2

 All the way
to London Town.

 All the way
to Jericho.

 All the way
to the Red Sea.

 All the way
to Blundellsands.

 All the way
to the bus stop.

 All the way
to Wester Ross.

 All the way
to Plymouth Sound.

 All the way
to the Isle of Wight.

 All the way
to King's Lynn.

 All the way
to Winnipeg.

 All the way
to Hong Kong.

 All the way
to Castlerigg.

Teachers' note See also page 101. Copy the rhyme cards on this page and those on page 101 onto card of different colours. The children begin each pair of lines of the skipping rhyme with a card from page 101 and complete it with a card from this page. They could make up other cards to add to the rhyme.

Developing Literacy
Poetry Compendium:
Ages 4–7
© A & C BLACK

Party poppers

• **Finish the pairs of party words.**
Their first sounds must be the same.

broken biscuits

crackly _____

_____ games

jiggly _____

_____ sandwiches

_____ lollipops

_____ toys

burst _____

_____ presents

_____ sweets

cheering _____

giggling _____

_____'s birthday

• **Make up some word-pairs about food.**
Example: chewy chocolate

Teachers' note Model the first four word-pairs (the first one has been completed), inviting the children to supply words which begin with the same sound: for example, broken biscuits, crackly crisps, great games, jiggly jelly. They could each word-process a word-pair, choosing a suitable font, size and style, for a class display of 'party poppers'.

**Developing Literacy
Poetry Compendium:
Ages 4–7
© A & C BLACK**

The horseman

- **Say the poem.**
- **Underline the rhyming words.**

Use a different colour for each rhyming sound.

The Horseman

I heard a horseman
Ride over the hill;
The moon shone clear,
The night was still;
His helm was silver,
And pale was he,
And the horse he rode
Was of ivory.

Walter de la Mare

Now try this!

- **Learn the poem.**

Look and read   Cover   Say   Check

- **What helps you to remember the words?**
- **Write the poem on the back of this sheet.**
- **Have you remembered it correctly?** ✓

Check

Teachers' note Read the poem with the children. Explain that 'helm' was a word used for 'helmet'. Re-read it and ask them to listen for anything which makes the poem easy to memorise. If necessary, emphasise the alliterative 'h' sounds in 'heard', 'horseman' and 'hill', and the end-of-line rhymes. The children could read the poem aloud in parts, each group reading two lines.

Developing Literacy
Poetry Compendium:
Ages 4–7
© A & C BLACK

What pictures do you see when you read these words?

• **Write and draw.**

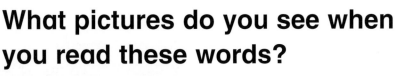

The words all come from real poems.

the forest's ferny floor	leaves a-shine with glistening drops of rain
<u>A shady place in a forest,</u> <u>with ferns growing.</u>	_____ _____ _____
a peacock with a fiery tail	(my sari) wraps round me like sunshine
_____ _____	_____ _____

Now try this!

• **Choose four** word-pictures **from poems you have read.**
• **Draw and label the pictures you see when you read them.**

Teachers' note Discuss evocative lines from poems the children have read (see **Notes on the activities**, page 89). Ask the children to describe the pictures which the lines conjure up. In the first example, ask them what the setting is, what they can 'see' there, what the atmosphere is like, the light, the colours and the sounds. Part of the description has been written; what can they add to it?

Developing Literacy
Poetry Compendium:
Ages 4–7
© A & C BLACK

Word-pictures: 2

- **Use this page to help you to write a word-picture.**

What is your word-picture about?

Title

Notes

Use a thesaurus.

Use a dictionary.

Write your ideas and useful words.

Description

Write in sentences.

- **Underline the important words in your description.**

See how much you can say in a few words.

Word-picture

Teachers' note The children should first complete the activity on page 105. Provide a subject for them to write about: for example, a painting, a flower, or a picture of a waterfall, cliffs or standing stones. Discuss the impression it makes on them and help them to find words to write about it.

Developing Literacy Poetry Compendium: Ages 4–7 © A & C BLACK

Sad sounds, happy sounds

- **Read the words a few times.
  Do they sound sad or happy?**
- **Write** sad **or** happy **in the boxes.**

My heart aches, and a drowsy numbness pains
My sense…

Everyone suddenly burst out singing.

…her yellow
laughter spilling
over…

We are like birds
with a broken wing.

…all at once I saw a crowd,
A host, of golden daffodils:
Beside the lake, beneath the trees,
Fluttering and dancing in the breeze.

Now try this!

- **Read the words again.**
- **Underline the sad or happy words in
  each sentence.**

Teachers' note Invite children who can to read the words while the others listen. Discuss the first
extract and ask the children if they think it sounds sad or happy. Can they explain why? Which
words are the most important in creating this feeling?

**Developing Literacy
Poetry Compendium:
Ages 4–7
© A & C BLACK**

Sad words, happy words

- **Sort the words into sad or happy words. Write them on the notepads.**

You could add other words which you find in poems.

broken	frisks	skip
cheer	glad	smiling
cold	no birds sing	sorrow
dancing	no one dances	sparkling
fallen	on my own	tearful
forlorn	singing	weeps

Sad words

Happy words

Now try this!

- **Choose a happy and a sad poem for a class** anthology **.**
- **Copy the poems in your best writing.**

Teachers' note The children should first complete the activity on page 107. Point out that they should include pairs or groups of words as well as single words: for example, 'no birds sing' sounds sad, but 'singing' sounds happy.

**Developing Literacy
Poetry Compendium:
Ages 4–7
© A & C BLACK**

Poets' words

Sometimes poets make up words.
- Cut out the cards.
- Match each word to its meaning.

Poets' words

crash-flash	eye-stretcher	glubbery
gratty	moan-faced	neat meat
ping-string	puff-fluff	slithy
snappermouth	wig-wag	yackle

Meanings

beefburger	cotton wool	crocodile
elastic	miserable	scratchy
slippery and slimy	sticky and oozing	surprise
tail	talk too much	thunderstorm

Now try this!

- **What do you think these made-up words mean?**

scrabby		flump		raggled

Teachers' note Introduce the activity by discussing words which describe the things they name, such as flip-flops, stick insect and bluebell, and invite the children to name others (they could prepare this for homework). During the plenary session, they could share the meanings they thought of for the words in the extension activity.

**Developing Literacy
Poetry Compendium:
Ages 4–7
© A & C BLACK**

Your own words

Imagine you don't know the names for these things. You can make up your own words!

• Write names which describe these things.

pricklebody　　　slimer

• **Make up words for these things you do.**

Now try this!

| hurry | sleep | drink | waste time |

Teachers' note Discuss the examples which have been completed and ask the children to explain them. Model the third example: encourage the children to think about what a hammer does, how it is used and the sound it makes. During the plenary session, they could share the words they have invented. The words could be word-processed, illustrated and displayed.

Developing Literacy Poetry Compendium: Ages 4–7
© A & C BLACK

110

Green poem

- **Read the poem.**

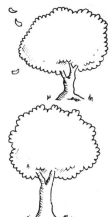

Green lettuce, green peas,

Green shade from green trees;

And grass as far as you can see,

Like green waves in a green sea.

Shirley Hughes

Here is another green poem.
It has the same pattern.

- **Fill in the gaps. Use the words from the box.**

| floor | pond | lime | cabbage | carpet |

Green _____, green _____,

Green _____ with green slime;

And moss across a rolling moor,

Like a green _____ on a green _____.

- **List six more green things.**
- **Re-write the first two lines of the poem.**
  Use words from your list.

Teachers' note Read the poem aloud and ask the children which words rhyme. Read it again, omitting the words 'trees' and 'sea'. Invite the children to supply them. Then read the second poem and the words in the box, and ask where each word could go. On an enlarged copy, record the children's ideas and invite them to read the completed verse aloud. Does it sound right? 'Green Lettuce, Green Peas' from *Colours* © 1986 Shirley Hughes.

Developing Literacy
Poetry Compendium:
Ages 4–7
© A & C BLACK

111

Red poem

• List some red things.

The pictures will help you to get started.

_____ _____

_____ _____

_____ _____

_____ _____

_____ _____

• Write a red poem. Fill in the gaps with words from your list.

Your poem need not rhyme.

Red _____, red _____,

Red _____ and red _____,

_____ _____ and red _____,

_____ _____ and red _____.

Now try this!

• Say your poem.

• Underline any words that rhyme.

Teachers' note The children should first complete the activity on page 111. This could be linked with work on colours: for example, by making a 'red corner' and collections of pictures of red things. Before the children do the activity, they could draw and write captions for red things. Ask them to say the names aloud. Provide a 'rhymes' word-bank from which they can choose words.

Developing Literacy Poetry Compendium: Ages 4–7 © A & C BLACK

Hump, jump, wiggle, jiggle

- **Say the poem.**
- **Circle the rhyming words.**

Use a different colour for each sound.

Jump or Jiggle

Frogs jump

Caterpillars hump

Worms wiggle

Bugs jiggle

Rabbits hop

Horses clop

Snakes slide

Seagulls glide

Mice creep

Deer leap

Puppies bounce

Kittens pounce

Lions stalk –

But –

I walk!

Evelyn Beyer

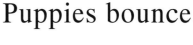 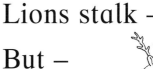 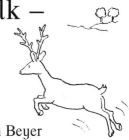

How do other animals move?
- **Write an animal in each gap.**

Now try this!

_____ walk

_____ nod

_____ spring

_____ stalk

_____ plod

_____ swing

Teachers' note Read the poem aloud, emphasising the rhyming words. Repeat it with the children joining in. Cover the words for the animals' movements and ask the children to recite the poem, including the missing words. For the extension activity, point out that the animals do not need to rhyme with, or begin with the same letter as, their actions.

Developing Literacy Poetry Compendium: Ages 4–7 © A & C BLACK

Crash, dash, rumble, tumble

How do these animals move?

• **Choose words from the word-bank.**

Use a dictionary.

cows	_____	dragonflies	_____
deer	_____	hedgehogs	_____
goats	_____	tortoises	_____
rats	_____	greyhounds	_____
lambs	_____	hares	_____
ducks	_____	swallows	_____

Word-bank

amble	dip	scrabble
dabble	flash	start
dart	gambol	stroll
dash	roll	trip

• **Put the animals and movements in rhyming pairs.**

Now try this!

_____   _____

_____   _____

_____   _____

_____   _____

Teachers' note The children should first complete the activity on page 113. They should look up any new words. In the main activity, encourage them to choose the words which best describe the animals' movement, regardless of rhyme. In the extension activity, they need to consider rhyme.

Developing Literacy Poetry Compendium: Ages 4–7 © A & C BLACK

Rats!

- **Say the poem. Listen to the first sounds of the words.**
- **In each line, underline the words with the same starting sound.**

Rats!

They fought the dogs and killed the cats,

  And bit the babies in the cradles,

And ate the cheeses out of the vats,

  And licked the soup from the cooks' own ladles,

Split open the kegs of salted sprats,

Made nests inside men's Sunday hats,

And even spoiled the women's chats,

   By drowning their speaking

   With shrieking and squeaking

In fifty different sharps and flats.

From *The Pied Piper of Hamelin* by Robert Browning

Now try this!

- **Say the poem again. Listen to the** ⬚ consonant ⬚ **sounds.**
- **Which do you hear the most often?** ⬚
- **Circle this sound in the poem.**

Work with a partner.

Teachers' note Read the poem and ask the children what they notice about the sounds in some lines (repeat the first line, emphasising the 'k/c' sounds of 'killed' and 'cats'). Can the children find repeated sounds at the beginnings of words in any other lines? For the extension activity, the children should read the poem aloud while a partner listens, and vice versa.

Developing Literacy
Poetry Compendium:
Ages 4–7
© A & C BLACK

Anthology: the sea

These lines are from poems about the sea.

- **Write some more on the shells.**

Write the title of the poem and the poet's name.

Sea Timeless Song

Sea timeless

Sea timeless

Grace Nichols

The Rime of the Ancient Mariner

The fair breeze blew, the white foam flew,

Samuel Taylor Coleridge

Teachers' note You could enlarge this page for the children, or for display. Remind the children of poems about the sea that they have read. Then select evocative lines from some poems and invite the children to choose their favourite lines from others. Encourage them to use contents pages and indexes of titles and first lines to find poems about the sea in poetry books.

**Developing Literacy
Poetry Compendium:
Ages 4–7
© A & C BLACK**

A poet

Poet's name _____

About the poet

Where was the poet born? Where does he or she live?

Poems I have read by this poet

My favourite

Topics which interest the poet

What does the poet often write about?

Anything special

Think about rhymes, other sounds, words.

Teachers' note Discuss a poet whose work the children have read at school. Help them to find information about the poet. Can they name any poems by him or her? What kind of things does the poet like to write about? Point out any special devices, such as alliteration, special use of punctuation, rhyme or invented words.

Developing Literacy
Poetry Compendium:
Ages 4–7
© A & C BLACK

One weird week

Listen to the starting sounds.

- **Fill in the gaps in the poem.**

made met model monster teeming terrible toad tickled trout tried	wet watched walked whale wing went Wales to thanked thief thistle threw thundery a	a fair to fairy found funny fish foggy to sad saw stormy snowy Saturday Spain sailed spider

One Sunny Sunday I saw a Snail;

One mad Monday I m_____ a m_____ ;

One t_____ Tuesday I t_____ at t_____ ;

One w_____ Wednesday I w_____

One th_____ Thursday I _____

_____ _____

One _____ Friday I _____

One _____

- **Make up another weird week poem.**

Now try this!

Teachers' note Read the first line of the poem and ask the children what they notice about the first sounds of some of the words. Model the second line with them and invite them to supply words to fill the gaps. The children could read their completed poems to a partner and circle the repeated sounds at the beginnings of words.

Developing Literacy
Poetry Compendium:
Ages 4–7
© A & C BLACK

Nonsense poems

This is silly. A sausage isn't a bird.

That's what makes it a nonsense poem!

The sausage is a cunning bird
With feathers long and wavy;
It swims about the frying pan
And makes its nest in gravy.

Anonymous

• **Make up the rest of this** nonsense poem.

The cabbage is a funny fish

With scales _____ ;

It _____

And _____ .

• **Write a** nonsense poem **about a biscuit.**

Now try this!

_____

_____

_____

_____

Teachers' note Introduce nonsense poems as poems which do not make sense ('non-sense'). Ask the children to point out any words which could be changed so that the poem *would* make sense (sausage, frying pan and gravy). In pairs, they could write a poem that does make sense, then change some of the words to turn it into a nonsense poem. The poems need not rhyme.

**Developing Literacy
Poetry Compendium:
Ages 4–7**
© A & C BLACK

Freeze, froze, sneeze, snooze

- **Read the poem. Circle the word that the poet made up.**

Ode to a Sneeze

I sneezed a sneeze into the air,

It fell to earth I know not where,

But hardened and froze the looks of those

In whose vicinity I snooze.

Anonymous

- **Make up some words of your own.**

freeze	froze	sneeze	*snoze*
speak	spoke	creak	
drink	drank	blink	
ride	rode	hide	
fly	flew	try	
shake	shook	make	
give	gave	live	

Now try this!

- **Make up four more words.**
- **Write a four-line poem which uses your words.**

Teachers' note Introduce the words 'ode' and 'vicinity' and let the children practise saying them. Discuss the ways in which verbs are changed to make the past tense: 'freeze'/'froze' (but not 'sneeze'/'snoze'); 'catch'/'caught' (but not 'match'/'maught') and so on.

Developing Literacy Poetry Compendium: Ages 4–7 © A & C BLACK

Ask a silly question

- **Write nonsense answers to the nonsense questions.**

 How many strawberries grow in the sea?

As many as herrings grow in the wood.

 Where do daffodils wash their feet?

In the place where roses comb their _____.

 When do worms buy new shoes?

On the day when caterpillars buy _____ _____.

 How do sausages tell the time?

In the same way that _____ _____.

What do elephants wear to a party?

The same as _____ _____.

 Now try this!

- **Write three nonsense questions for a partner to answer.**

Teachers' note As a whole-class activity, play a 'silly question and answer' game in which you (or a child) ask a silly question which invites a silly, but corresponding, answer: for example, 'How do fish brush their teeth?' / 'In the same way that snails comb their hair,' and so on.

Developing Literacy
Poetry Compendium:
Ages 4–7
© A & C BLACK

Riddle match

- **Match the riddles to the answers.**

Riddle	1	2	3	4	5	6
Answer	A					

1 What is black and white and read?

2 What is yours but is used mainly by other people?

3 What has a bed on which no one sleeps?

A  a newspaper	B water	C a bar of soap
D your name _____	E a bell 	F the sea

4 What runs but has no legs?

5 What gets smaller as it gets older?

6 What has a ring but no finger?

- **Work out the answer to this riddle.**

Now try this!

I look the same as you;
You look the same as me.
When I see you, you see me.
I do whatever you do,
But my right is the left of you.

Anonymous

Teachers' note Read other examples of riddles to the children and help them to work out the answers. Encourage them to think of several possible answers for each riddle and then to choose the one that is the best match.

Developing Literacy
Poetry Compendium:
Ages 4–7
© A & C BLACK

Riddle-me-ree

Each line of the riddle tells you one letter of the answer.

- **Write the letters.**
- **Write the answer.**

The last line gives you a clue.

Riddle	Letter
Look once in roast and twice in toast,	t
Then in bacon and in taken,	
Then in baking but not in taking.	
My fourth is in lamb but not in ham;	
My fifth and last is in least but not last,	
And I'll come to your feast but not your fast.	

Answer _____

Now try this!

- **Write one-line riddles for these letters.**

Use pairs of words which go together, like sing and sang.

a _____

b _____

d _____

e _____

Teachers' note The children should first have experience of reading and working out riddles and should have completed the activity on page 122. Explain that this page is about riddles which spell a word. Point out that some lines offer more than one possible answer; the children should write down all the possibilities and wait until they have all the others before deciding which is correct.

Developing Literacy Poetry Compendium: Ages 4–7 © A & C BLACK

Riddle writer

- **Write a riddle to spell** `drum` **.**
- **Make up a clue for the last line.**

You could use some of these words.

Word-bank

any	dog	her	many	rung
black	down	him	meat	sing
blue	eat	hog	out	street
car	few	horse	rat	sung
cart	go	in	ring	up
come	goat	lane	road	van

My first is in dog, but not in _____

My second is _____

_____

My third is _____

_____

My fourth is _____

_____

| Clue | _____ |

Now try this!

- **Write a riddle for another word.**
- **Give it to a partner to solve.**

Teachers' note The children should first have experience of reading and working out riddles and should have completed the activities on pages 122 and 123. Encourage them to choose pairs of words for each line which go together in some way (such as 'horse' and 'cart'). Some children might be able to word-process their riddles for a class display.

**Developing Literacy
Poetry Compendium:
Ages 4–7**
© A & C BLACK

Tongue-twister kit: 1

Rory licked a lolly;

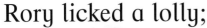

A wicked worker walked to Wales;

A rabbit lived in a warren;

A green goblin gobbled gooseberries

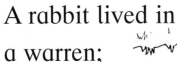

Ten tired travellers talked

The bull bellowed at Brenda

Quickly count the questions

Winnie wore bright red wellies

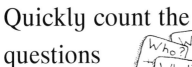

Twelve treacle tarts

Nicola knitted with nine needles

She sold sausages

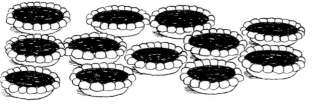

Jack jiggled a jelly;

Teachers' note Cut out the cards (which could be copied onto card and laminated for re-use). The second part of each tongue-twister is on a card on page 126. The children match the halves and say the tongue-twisters. Continued on page 126.

Developing Literacy
Poetry Compendium:
Ages 4–7
© A & C BLACK

125

Tongue-twister kit: 2

The lolly Rory licked was lime.

From Wick to Wrexham the worker walked.

A wild rabbit with waggling whiskers.

Growing on a green gooseberry bush.
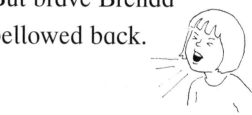

As they trekked two by two on the track.
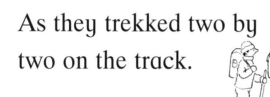

But brave Brenda bellowed back.

In the Queen's Christmas quiz.

For riding in wet weather.

Trickled treacle on the table.
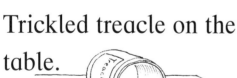

But her knitting was knotty and never neat.
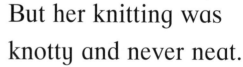

In the sausage shop.
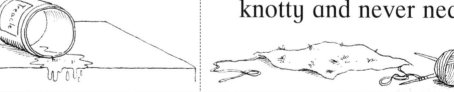

Jack jogged to Japan.

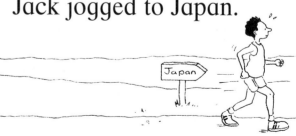

Teachers' note Continued from page 125. During the plenary session ask the children which phoneme makes each tongue-twister difficult to say.

Developing Literacy Poetry Compendium: Ages 4–7 © A & C BLACK

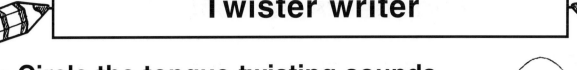

Twister writer

- **Circle the tongue-twisting sounds.**
- **Complete each tongue-twister. Use the same sounds.**

Felicity Fettler, forty and fit

Feasted with fifty fortunate ferrets.

Deepak's dog dug deep

_____

Betty Buckle bought a bucket

_____

Seven spinning spiders

_____

Charlie chased chickens

_____

Bella bought broken bricks

_____

Shelley saw a shiny shoe

_____

I see icicles

_____

Now try this!

- **Choose one of the tongue-twisters.**
- **Write three more lines.**

Teachers' note The children should first complete the activities on pages 125–126. Model the first example with them and ask them which sounds they should repeat (the 'f' sound at the beginning of a word and the 't' sound at the end or in the middle). Some children might be able to word-process their tongue-twisters for a class display.

Developing Literacy
Poetry Compendium:
Ages 4–7
© A & C BLACK

Word-juggler jokes

- **Join the questions to the answers.**

Answers

Tweethearts!

Be quiet while I'm spooking.

Up his sleevies!

1. What did the mother ghost say to her son while she was talking on the telephone?

2. Where did the general keep his armies?

3. What do you call two birds kissing?

- **Change the words to make funny answers.**

What is the world's brainiest mountain?

_____

Where do spooks buy stamps?

_____

What do pigs put on cuts?

_____

What is a horse's favourite game?

_____

Mount Everest

The Post Office

Ointment

Table tennis

Now try this!

- **Write two more word-juggler jokes.**
- **Try them out on a partner.**

Teachers' note Discuss the jokes with the children and ask them to point out the ways in which words have been changed: for example, sweethearts/tweethearts and speaking/spooking. In the second part of the activity, encourage the children to think of ways to alter the words.

Developing Literacy
Poetry Compendium:
Ages 4–7
© A & C BLACK